Part 1

Part 2

Richard,
the
enjoy
brother
prose

J. Montgomery

"and if my thought-dreams could be seen,

they'd probably put my head in a guillotine"

1

This Land is Thailand

Ready, Fire, Aim

This time is going to be different. Had I tried to hop this flight a few years ago they would've thrown me right back in the nut house. In the suburbs of America being spontaneous and unpredictable can come across as offensive to polite society. They're all still going to think I'm crazy for not mowing the lawn, sitting at traffic lights, and watching the evening news like a normal person, but I can't fake it anymore. I have zero regrets about trading in the creature comforts and stability of that life for an easy chair in row 67, westbound over the Pacific Ocean.

Doubtful I get any sleep in this seat. It's comfortable enough, but the movie selection is too good, and for some reason, alcoholic beverages are free on this flight. "Um, yes please, and make it a double if you would be so kind". She's such a darling. There's no way this airline makes money by taking me on as a passenger. Honestly though, who cares. I'm just a man with a head full of thoughts hitching a ride to nowhere in particular. People do this sort of thing all the time, right? Backpacking, globe trekking, world-shaking... smooth sailing.

I wonder if the guy sitting next to me has any idea that I'm certifiably insane. Through a series of completely predictable events, I find out that his name is Casey, and that he has no idea at all... about anything. His mind is blown by the idea that I could impulsively buy a one-way ticket to an unknown place with no plan of what exactly I'm going to do once I get there. He's in his twenties, was born in Thailand, but has lived in the USA for the last decade or so. He works in Silicon Valley

4

making computer chips or something like that. He's part of a huge collective over there slaving away for the man 70 hours a week, sacrificing some of the best years of his life to his company. Poor bastard. It wasn't so long ago that I was in his shoes. I forget why I drove myself crazy chasing that cheese. How do we as self-aware beings motivate to live in the pursuit of such abstract goals?

It's in our culture now to work ourselves to exhaustion, but at this point in history, I think a person should be able to carry their weight in society by working 3 days a week. I realize I sound like a dreamer saying that, but the tools and machines of today can accomplish pretty much any job 20 times faster and more accurately than in the recent past. Yet we all work more than we did back then. Why? The houses are already built, the cars are made by robots, and agriculture practically harvests itself with today's mechanical efficiencies and chemical compounds.

The customs agent at the arrival gate sure seems to be curious about the purpose of my trip. I don't know man, I'm just trying to have a good time and take a look around the place. I can't say that of course, so I just point to the box I checked that says tourism. What's he going to do, lock me up for seeming out of place? Of course, I'm out of place. I don't speak the language, hold any currency, know where I am, or where I'm going. Clearly, I'm just another stupid American tourist walking around like I own the place. Excuse me gentlemen, just passing through.

I pocket my passport and all the scraps of paper he gives me all marked up with his fancy stamps. Casey's a bit disoriented since he hasn't been here in 15 years, but he's figuring it out better than I am. He knows the language and has somewhat of an idea about how to ride the train from the airport into the city. I feel a bit awkward following him, but I have no other sense of direction at this point, and no real first destination anyway. Casey is just going to have to be my spirit guide for now.

I'm quickly realizing how underprepared I am. I'm a foreign man in a foreign land wandering around with the overstuffed backpack that I hastily loaded up on the other side of the globe in a spring snowstorm high in the Rocky Mountains of Colorado. There's a fraction of an instinct to want to quit at this point and throw in the towel, but since this's not really an option, this day becomes all about forward momentum. Baby steps. Go to a place that serves food, sit down, get a beer. Next, hook into some wi-fi and find a hostel or some next destination. Move to the next checkpoint that seems to make sense. Sit down, grab a beer, observe routine interactions and start to appreciate the local flavor. Keeping beer as a goal throughout the day tends to help make things happen. My goal now is basically to find some lodging. It's a standard moon walk operation - find an initial place to unpack, plant a flag of victory, then take a nap.

A friend of mine was in Bangkok a few years earlier and recommended the "Q" hotel. He looks like a happy Italian Jesus, laughs like a baby bird and has the legs of a 1980's tennis player. Not much else remarkable about him, except that he speaks 9 different languages and has a Ph.D. in astrophysics. Somehow I find my way to the Q, check in and sleep the sleep of a dreamer. The last few chapters of my waking life sweep by as they tend to do for everyone I guess. On my way from Colorado to Thailand, I had a day and a half layover in Seattle. It was my first time there. Nice town but shitty weather. Cold and wet like the brochure says, and most of the people that live there are trendy hipsters. Their aquarium sucks, underground market is cool, the Space Needle is dumb, bar scene seems okay. Suicide capital of America. Coffee town.

Jet lag is a funny thing. I wake with the crow pre-dawn. After twelve hours of hard dreaming, it's 4 am and I'm wide awake. Day 2 in Bangkok, in a hotel in some part of an ancient city that I'm completely unfamiliar with. I have myself a shit, shower, shave, and shampoo; but not in that order... and I don't shave anyway. I take inventory of the belongings and supplies that found their way with me to this point in time and space. I assess the situation and assemble a loose plan to head out and explore Bangkok. It's hot as balls here, so the first thing I do is cut the arms and legs off of all my clothes. I hope all the people I meet like my newly fashioned jorts.

There's a water taxi stop behind the Q just as Italian Jesus the babiest of birds had described. With my mastery of deciphering various forms of broken English, I have learned from the man at the front desk that the boat can get me to the heart of town. As it turns out, the front desk guy is also the cook, maid, valet, and probably a woman sometimes.

Safety standards aren't the same here as in America. They don't tell you how the water taxi works and it's not obvious where the boat stop is either. I watch one boat go by from the wrong pier. Then I watch people get on and off the next boat without it really coming to a stop. With daft skill and reckless abandonment I'm able to hurl myself aboard the next craft... just like the 60-year-old woman next to me carrying groceries and a baby.

It's a nice ride into the heart of Bangkok, on this back alley canal. I guess you could call it a canalley if you were so inclined. I can see the back of everyone's houses and shacks. Laundry hanging off of every ledge and rail but never drying in the humid polluted air. Cats and chickens are everywhere. The graffiti is amazing. So much interesting trash in the water. This place has it all!

I don't know where I'm going, but it doesn't matter. The un-aimed arrow never misses. I get to what seems like half way to somewhere when everyone gets off the boat, so I get off with them. At times like this, I'm so glad I'm traveling solo. The process of learning and making instinctual decisions is just not the same when it has to be discussed or thought through or decided upon in any logical way. I guess most of these people are headed into work. There's a mega mall here. Well, I guess it's more of a mother ship that mega malls might orbit around. It's enormous, like ten city blocks, like the size of a pill factory in suburban Pennsylvania. The people that I get off the boat with don't work at the mother ship mall though, they work in the asteroid belt of street carts selling food and nick knacks to folks walking around outside this behemoth temple of modern inequality. Inside the mall, it's a comfortable 76 degrees of fresh air. Outside, at 7 am, it is 95 degrees, humid as hell and so polluted that even the people smoking cigarettes are putting face masks on between drags.

It's still early morning, I'm not yet in a tourist zone, but I've been up for hours so I sample some of this street food. I can't tell what anything is, but it doesn't matter since each plate is just as foreign as the next, so I just get with the guy in front of me gets. Delicious, whatever it is. I like my food like I like my women - mysterious and delicious. Hold the mayo.

There is quite a buzz around this dock, but I look at the map and see that I'm still outside the heart of town. I can't figure why everyone had to get off the ferry, then on to the next to get all the way into the city. The next raft comes tearing down the canal, loud as hell, blowing smoke everywhere, and we all hop on when it bumps up against the pier and comes as close to a stop as it's going to get.

When I get off in town I see all the local swindlers swarm to the tourists like flies to blood and shit. I think I'm fairly incognito, but walking down the street, looking this way and that, I'm clearly seen by these guys as a potential gold mine. Wouldn't you know it, I'm befriended by one of them. Lin is an English teacher, a do-gooder that just happens to be waiting for the light to change at the same corner as me. It's Buddha day, he says. Lucky day, very special, I drive you, he says. He tells me his service is free today and that he works for me now. Lucky day indeed.

I get in his tuk-tuk which is basically half motorcycle and half wagon. Again, the safety standards aren't like they are in the USA. Traffic is total chaos and everyone is buzzing around on these motorized tricycles with no helmets or harnesses, swerving between tuks, buses, beat up cars and the occasional Ferrari the entire way.

Lin is chain smoking this whole time. He knows English well enough but isn't a talker or laugher. All business. I think for a second that maybe he's kidnapping me, but eventually we get to one of the monuments I had circled on the map that I picked up earlier in my hotel lobby. Well well well, what do we have here, this must be the world famous giant gold statue of Buddha. Amazing. What a devoutly religious community that must have erected this temple I think to myself. As we drive from point to point I come to realize that there are hundreds of these temples, each one boasting that their Buddha is the biggest and goldenest.

I keep expecting Lin to leave me alone, but every time I come out of these touristy places he's still waiting for me. I tell him I'm going to go my own way for now, but he won't leave, he's mine for the day he says. Strange. I feel that it would be rude to decline, so we continue on. Buddha day, no entry fee, lucky day. Clearly a scam coming, but whatever, who cares.

You have to give it to these guys, amazing cold call sales people. They will literally approach a thousand people an hour with a very friendly but aggressive sale, and there are fifty of them down every street. They offer all sorts of things as you walk by, and won't take no for an answer. You might be sitting there and a girl comes up to you to sell you a bracelet or a wooden frog, and just smiles and points to her wares. To say you're not interested, or no thank you, or wave them away is received to them as an invitation to show more items. They will then set their bag down to pull out more knick knacks. Before you know it, three other people smell blood in the water and come up to sell their pieces too. It feels unnatural, but the only way to avoid these situations is to actively ignore them.

After a bite to eat we go to something Lin describes as "high fashion". This region has a reputation for high quality tailored suits for cheap. The Bangkok parasites take advantage of this reputation by trying to sell to people that think they are getting a smoking hot deal.

I see what's going on here, and kind of feel bad knowing that this guy is wasting his time driving me around all day. I have no intention of buying anything. So I go along with his insistence that I visit the suit store. It's a random experience, I have nowhere else to be, what the hell. I'm as immune to pressure sales as I am to guilt trips. They have many similarities. They put the target in a position where they have to be defensive about being either dumb or heartless to say no. One uses logic, the other uses emotion. When someone pulls this kind of trap on me I usually feel out their premise and put it back on them. There's a good bit of self-delusion involved in trying to guilt or con someone, so when you expose people to themselves they will often feel a general discomfort known as cognitive dissonance and they won't like you, the same way you don't like food that makes you sick.

In the second suit shop, a girl and I notice each other. They clearly dragged her there too. She's an easier target for sure. Big fish. She's carrying a giant traveler's backpack and an expensive camera around her neck. She's a young, pretty, blond-haired girl with a thick British accent. In the gem shop that each of our "lucky day" tuk-tuk drivers takes us to next, we recognize each other again and talk about how ridiculous this tour is getting. With some assistance, I'm able to convince my indentured servant that I'm pairing up with this girl. Her whip is much better anyway - a big pink tuk-tuk with colored lights and tassels hanging down.

It's day one in this country for both of us. Great gal, a perfect travel companion. She's just a tumbling tumbleweed out here like I am, drifting on down the stream, over the rapids, and into the great delta. Delta Montgomery.

The Kiwi Chronicles

It's a staring contest back at her hostel that sets us in motion together. Quite a trick if I do say so myself. It was all her idea. I don't think it's her first time pulling this move. It's quite an experience. There's an ambiguous intensity of staring someone in the eye which can feel simultaneously invasive and vulnerable.

After this little waltz of our open minds, we get to talking about our day. She asks about the signature I was using in the registries at the temples we visited. It's some stupid symbol I came up with back in college around the first time I completely lost my mind. It's basically a tilted Sigma with a dot on the side. It kind of looks like a simple stick figure drawing of the profile of a person with a big nose like me. If you sort of break the symbol apart a few different ways it spells "love". Seemed an appropriate mark to bring back out into the world today. When I draw it out on a piece of paper to illustrate this it resulted in the words "love love" written at the top of the page. The next morning I notice she had a tattoo. It says "love love". She tells me it's something she and her mum used to say to each other all the time before she died about a year ago. I couldn't have known that when we did the sketch last night. So it seemed that right off the bat we have acquired some sort of blessing from the Buddha and her dear mother ghost.

Unlike me, she has an itinerary all mapped out already. Before I met up with her yesterday, her lucky tuk-tuk driver had already gotten her to drop an obscene amount of cash on a 3-week tour of the country. The travel agent he took her to booked hotels, busses, trains, jungle tours and all sorts of things. I had no intention to go inland. I'm more interested in the islands to the south. But since I have no specific plans yet, and this little blondie from New Zealand is throwing out the idea of going north with her, I figure why not. It's all new to me anyway so what's the difference. Same same.

So north ends up being the hand that pulls me. It's nice to get the hell out of Bangkok. From that chaos comes loose direction. Still very turbulent and unpredictable, but with a sense of order and tempo. This kiwi seems happy but generally aloof; as content and casual about our little affair as I am. But as we travel her story starts to unravel. She tells me she dropped out of med school and grad school, and she used to be a lingerie model, and in the air force. She tells me she dreams lucidly, that she controls her dreams; flies whenever she wants. I'm realizing that this is her bubble world, and the rest of us are just moving through it.

I guess they have a king in this country. His picture is everywhere. He seems like a real dork. Skinny, glasses, awkward looking. It's actually illegal to make jokes about him, but it's too easy. His picture is on all the money, and in one of the bills he has a huge camera around his neck like a stereotypical Asian tourist. Hilarious. You can tell the locals here love him though. Apparently no one knows where he is these days. He's not at the royal palace - that's just a building for tourists to walk around now.

The small towns are nice, but dang they have a lot of temples here. It's pretty absurd especially when you consider the level of sin and debauchery in this country - prostitution capital of the world. But I guess Buddhism isn't too concerned with that. According to something I read on the internet or in a book this week about 90% of the population considers themselves Buddhist, and take their faith seriously. I can't see how they can rectify one with the other. Well, I guess right wing Christian conservative Republicans are able to hold to capitalism and nationalistic righteousness sacred while at the same time praying to a peace and poverty-loving voice in their heads. I think what it comes down to is that we all want to feel justified. It's never easy to quiet the voices and relax the constructs in our minds. I think some people stack these polar ideas in their heads against each other so tightly that to even think of backing off the pile of bullshit is enough strife and stress to just shut the mind down to handle only the most routine basic functions. Well, that's basically the polarized packed in bullshit I tell myself to keep my own self-righteous defense mechanisms up too I guess. To tear that down would mean backing out of about 10 years of perception. What would be the point of falling into that abyss?

12

It seems that along with a penchant for cocaine and casual sex, my travel partner here has laid out a tip-top expedition into the Thailand jungle; just capital. I myself am on a trip, a departure from my ways and tendencies. Hopefully I'll be moving back to a rebirth in my home port that I love so dearly, but's hard to say when the return will be. 2 weeks, 2 months. I don't know anyone out here and no one knows me, thus perfect conditions for my transformation. I doubt this companion of mine knows that she is my muse. I believe that for both creative and pragmatic reasons I have led us both to believe that she is my new love interest.

If we were dogs I'd playfully chase her around. She'd be bigger but not shy or submissive. I'd roll over on my back and expose my belly. She'd get bored and walk away. Master would like me better, but she would garner more attention like the prissy little bitch that she is. But of course we roll in the grass at our leisure enjoying the fulfillment of our carnal pleasures. Then I kiss her face for a while and talk sweetly about tender feelings before she again applies that death grip on my throat with her razor sharp teeth. Standard play time.

We're on a bus going from Sukhothai to Chiang Mai when it occurs to me that she has a lot of the traits of a classic borderline personality. I'm somewhat qualified to make this assessment after studying the topic while a grad student at the Funny Farm School of Hard Knocks; a very formative institution. From what I remember about borderline, it usually manifests as a swell of the need for affection until that affection is given. At that point, they will villainize you, put you on the defensive, make wild accusations, yell at you and treat you like trash until you ditch them. Then they apologize profusely, claim they can't live without you, they love you more than life itself and need you. These might be welcome words to a person who stuck through the torture of the bad times, but buyer beware. The tide will slam ashore as intensely as it went out. These girls ain't messing around. They play the role of victim well. When shit goes sideways they often end up with black eyes and their men and end up in jail. Borderline personality disorder is an often studied dynamic in the field of psychology. I too am an often studied subject in the field of psychology - of the more bipolar variety.

The borderline behavior starts in childhood and is more common in girls than boys. They will often be the kind of kid that will stand on the sofa while a parent is in the room and intentionally fall head first to the ground. If the parent doesn't catch them, they would hit the floor hard causing themselves great harm. A parent couldn't forgive themselves if they let this happen. But how do you make the kid stop? These kids grow into beautiful girls with the same tendencies. The difference is, eventually the world doesn't care if they fall on their face. In fact the grown woman may notice that her world is cheering her demise. After a few big falls, it becomes hard to watch. Some look away, but not me. I like to watch, not for spite or entertainment but for curious interest. I've been burned by behavior like this enough to be able to separate emotionally. It's not easy though. I am a soft carrying empathetic soul. Often times, they are as well. But I am my only safety net now. I would share it, but not with someone that would destroy it. In this case I must keep my guard up for the next few days before I part with this girl. I've enjoyed her company for the most part, but sense that as I ignore her as I plan to do she will come on to me again. If this happens it would be hard for me to reject her advances.

I wonder how the dynamic of borderline personality women changes when they have children. I should look into that. The study of psychology fascinates me, almost as much as economics. They make me daydream lucidly. For now I'll just put on my iPod, look out the bus window and watch Thailand pass by. How about a little Dylan mix. Like a Rolling Stone - his classic hit about a girl that has fallen on her face. Love Minus Zero No Limit - a psychedelic ballad about that sweet euphoric time when you first meet that flighty girl. Just Like a Woman, Queen Jane, One More Cup of Coffee. I think I read somewhere that he's written and recorded over 800 songs. Groovy.

It's funny to think that pretty much every square inch of every town, city or farm is owned by somebody. Like there's a piece of paper for all that land and property connecting it to some person or group. To anyone that "owns" land it becomes a piece of their existence. They will often define themselves by it. Drive around town, even the shitty parts… especially the shitty parts - somebody owns that run down shack, weed-filled lawn, or empty parking lot. And somehow when you put all these pieces together, all the humans that are responsible for these spaces lay them out and organize them like an organism. The city grid is an organism. Our self-awareness leads us to take ownership of this space; sometimes by force. But in the long run, we come and go as the organism dictates. "I can't start a family till I get a job, I should plant a tree here and put in a shed, I should blow up this building, I need a windmill here". These very common human decisions are driven by something innate to us all, and these instincts that are all similar in every human physically create a world that is just as similar everywhere.

Sex, alcohol, drugs, love, country, God, passion, debt, service, trust, money, commitment, insanity, emotion, shelter, intelligence, friends, lovers, possession, war, peace, food - the list goes on and on. These things have nothing in common except that they are ideas that drive our world. We as individuals have triumphs and struggles with all these phantom abstracts. As a collective these constructs define our existence. Settlements along rivers, currency, leader selection, circles and squares seen from the sky. What is it? According to the Delta Montgomery Micro Astrological Analogy Department, the apparatus driving the whole machine is the Golgi apparatus. And every apparatus has a cellular function made of DNA double helix spectrums of thought and existence. When the Golgi thinks flowers, man builds a garden in hopes of love, wealth, self-discovery, for scientific research, or avoidance of reality. Or whatever. This is complete nonsense.

This girl is a freak in plain clothes and rainbows man. Hard yet fragile like a diamond. Positively 4th street. She's running away from something, a past that I believe she will eventually shake. She's strong and stubborn; charming and beautiful. She has some real dangerous habits. Maybe that's what she's running from.

But I'm not on this trip for her. We just met. This trip is for me. She entertains me, interests me. I want to get to know her, but not get wrapped up in her web. This itinerary of her's that I've latched onto has given me direction out here, forward momentum, great pictures and memories, safety and stability. I like to think that maybe she gets a peace of mind about me being around as well.

I wonder how life is for you my dear. Love love. Your mom died when you were 20. Cancer. Your dad is estranged. A fiancé at 19. Cheated on you. Broke your heart I suppose. 2 years of drugs and sex. Your sister is 20 years old now with a 5-year-old son. When you get down to it though, you're still a young willow wisp of a girl. I'm more than happy to drink what you pour before they make last call.

Halfway to Tuesday

Of the backpacker life - a submission the open roads, rails, airplanes, and hostels along the breadcrumbs of discovery of humanity. The itinerary of the day usually starts with the person that just sat down next to you at your breakfast of bread and coffee. A casual conversation that leads out the front door together toward wherever makes sense to go to today. Sure, why not. There is an exploration of each other and the city or countryside paradise that you find yourself in. There's an appreciation for the subtleties of each other's familiar and foreign languages as little thoughts and observations naturally turn into discussions of the age-old mysteries of mankind.

Are you hungry? Sure, let's pop into this little place. A family of indigenous people greet you and feed you like they've done for several years for all of the world travelers that now frequent their world with the routine of a gust of wind. The children look in amazement at the silly hats and shoes of the foreigners that aren't foreign to them at all since they've seen these visitors their entire lives.

You fumble through a handful of colorful monetary notes with exaggerated numbers trying to do the math of how many thousands of units of the local currency you're supposed to leave on the table. Even though the cost of breakfast is higher than the amount of money their grandparents paid for land, beasts, and tools of trade a generation ago, they barely seem to care about that detail where you are. 2000 units for an egg. Just let the children have practice at the calculator. Often with no schooling or the ability to read, they speak English as well as their native tongue by the lessons that the open observation of this backpacker route has given them.

Backpacking really has nothing to do with the luggage. When I first heard the description a couple decades ago, I pictured hauling your belongings around all month, hitch hiking across a barren desert, or ancient city where you clearly don't belong. But in reality, you carry your luggage out of the airport, get in a bus or taxi, get out at the random hostel you booked a couple days ago, go upstairs, unload and secure your things in your room, take a shower, change your clothes and go outside to stroll around for some lunch or a drink. The entire place is basically foreign, and there's plenty to observe even just from the front steps of your temporary new residence. And while sitting there, the person you met a few days ago or a few years ago comes up and you pick a direction to walk or go back inside to play cards or have a cup of coffee as the next set of travelers rolls through.

How long are you traveling for, where were you last, where are you from, how long are you going to be here, where to next, what are you doing today; the standard routine introduction that always leads to several crossovers of experience, and usually a friend for the day or a lifetime. I suppose I'll write a book about it. It'll very generally be about people that live in a dream world all their own.

Lying next to her unable to sleep processing the things she told me last night. 3somes, routine one night stands, strap on stuff, sex isn't anything to her she says, just for fun. Slept with 50 people, maybe 100 is her guess. It's kind of hot in a way I guess, like banging a porn star, but it's mostly repulsive. 23 years old. Drug of choice - ecstasy of course. Used to enjoy shoplifting too, just for the thrill. She always uses condoms. I should have known something was up when I saw a bag of like 200 of them in her pack. I thought it was a gag gift from a friend.

If you can give your body so freely, where does the guarded heart take shelter? Does it water down the passion of truer love? Are you more cautious about a hug then a fuck? Or have you just been along for the ride all this time? Are you driving, navigating, or just floating downstream. What has this lifestyle given you and shown you? What has it taken? With so many lovers, are you aware of any of the broken hearts I'm sure you have left in your wake? Do you ever feel guilty about it, proud; anything besides indifference? You may say they should have known better, but you're too charming to be forgotten. I should know, but I can already see the void that will be left when we part. That's just me though, it doesn't take much for me to torment myself.

Like any other intoxication, there's a price to be paid at the end. But there's also a chance that there is no end. There are parallel universes where we continue on together for a long long time, even forever. It's well within the realm of possibility, especially considering the magical way we started or journey.

I know that inevitably you'll take a lover for your life. Why? What will he give you in exchange for your freedom? Challenge maybe. It would be a cold man that could deny the rarity of your nature. They're the ones you go for though, am I right? I imagine I'm not the only one who may dream of what your future may be like. We've all seen happy and tragic outcomes for special people like you - untamed wild free spirits. This is a special trip for you; a journey that could have been put off until it was too late, or one that might last too long...

Yeah, we were just talking, ya know, partying at the bungalow last night, revealing secrets as passing lover strangers do I guess. Getting deep. I guess a girl like that gets it and doesn't judge... that's what she said when I told her about all the times they locked me up in the loon bin. She said people could judge her on her choices too, and that my troubles weren't actually of my choosing. Still, here we are, I judge. I judge harsh. Maybe too harsh. Maybe this is an exercise in open-mindedness. I often hold it against women when I find out about their sexual past. I really shouldn't I suppose.

The stigma of having been in a mental hospital is so heavy. Even the most open-minded person that's known you for years will treat you different when they find out you've spent months in and out the grinder of those hellish institutions. Obviously it's a major red flag to anyone thinking of being in a relationship when they find out that their partner has spent weeks at a time in solitary confinement, or has been repeatedly wrestled to the ground and held down to receive an injection of sedative. It's rare to not end up falling down the rabbit hole again and again once things get that intense. Even during the years of normalcy between lock-ups you have to live with not just the underlying emotional frailty, but also with the PTSD of still being in those dark places in your mind. Knowing that your friends and family will never look at you the same way again; that they will always have one finger on the dial ready to call the cops to take you away again for the dozenth time.

Maybe I shouldn't have spilled the beans. She was telling me all the heavy details of her life though, and it just seemed right. Every time I tell someone about that stuff I wish I hadn't. I even admitted that basically I'll be preemptively writing her off to an extent. I can't help it anymore. It's just a natural self-defense mechanism born from the experience of being suddenly disregarded so often.

It's an open line of communication we have now. I doubt her feelings and perceptions of me have changed much since we first met, but mine of her is dramatically different. She's a different breed... or maybe not. There are thousands and thousands of pretty, charming, exotic, girls out there - unique, like everyone else. She's a femme fatale. I wonder where her mind is on this kinship we have. Does it feel rare or special to her? What does this girl look for in a man? She's single now and has no obligation to me. Yet we travel together. Looking back, passing kisses haven't meant what I thought they meant at the time. The staring contest was a ruse. Or maybe not. I don't know. Today is a new day and we're on a bus to a new town.

I think it's easy for girls like her to brush their past under the carpet when they've had enough. If they want, they can shift gears and land themselves a sucker husband and turn into money grubbing miserable bitch wives. I've seen this transformation happen over and over. They'll blame their men for making them settle when all they wanted to do was be a free spirit and travel the world. I'm pretty sure that this little missy thinks she's better than me, better than everyone. She thinks it's her world and we all just live in it. Maybe it's all in my head, who knows. Either way, she'll still be a good travel companion for now.

It's easy to just roll along with everything since we're in such a foreign place. Even after all the intense discussions about the past, she still has a very honest warmth about her. We're having a mid-day drink in town when news comes across the TV screen that the queen of England or princess or whatever just had a baby girl. I'm stunned to see tears rolling down her face. She's from there originally and still has a pretty nice British accent. It's sweet. Oh, and one of her front teeth is a little crooked and it melts my heart to look at every time. Her tender emotion caught me by surprise though. I just can't figure out this little butterfly.

I'm definitely doing more on this trip than I otherwise would have if we didn't meet, but I'm thinking that maybe I'll part ways with her at the Thailand - Laos border and make my way over to Vietnam. That was my goal on this trip initially. That's the deep end of the pool that I was trying to swim out to. Her plan is to backtrack south to Bangkok again, then over to Cambodia. She thinks that after she travels around for a couple months she'll stay out here and teach English. It seems that's what people talk about doing now when they aspire to break away from the shackles of society.

This place can be more than a little intimidating at times. I take a walk away from our latest dwelling place toward the main street of town. Along the way, I hear terrifying aggressive growls. I look across the street and see a pack of wild dogs attacking each other viciously for about 5 minutes. Fortunately, they're in some sort of fenced in abandoned building. There are stray dogs everywhere in this country. Some are aggressive like this pack, and others shake and cower in fear of humans as they have obviously been brutally beaten their entire lives. Wild animals are just like humans in their response to a beat down from a cruel world. Fight or flight... or fright.

About 10 times a day on this trip I find myself wandering into some garden, temple, restaurant, or cafe, and falling into a simple conversation with a local or a fellow traveler. I roll right along with it because what else are you going to do? But sometimes I think of the people in my life that would be mesmerized by just one minute of this

21

type of interaction. Years ago, strapped to a desk and my college degrees, moving rapidly toward a mortgage in some suburb, I couldn't imagine living a random day like this. It felt like it was all over for me and I had to accept the future as a list of to-do items. That mindset is like a fuzzy memory.

From that pathetic point, my life fell apart... thank god. This life I've fallen into wouldn't have been possible without all the pitfalls and failures I've gotten myself into. You don't get here without some propensity to overindulge or follow the white rabbit where she might lead. But to experience it and come out on the other end is a very special thing; unique to us all.

Don't get me wrong, I'm not some better-than-you hippie thinking I've chosen this path because I'm so cunning and adventurous... well maybe a little. But in reality I may have been happier not flunking out of life over and over again. It's quite possible that I may have felt more fulfilled experiencing the stability of a life partner and grounded routine that has eluded me all this time.

The origin of money in the most theoretical sense was a way to measure your benefit to society. You could then cash in that benefit for goods and services that others could provide in return. Since it's invention though there's been a constant exploitation of the power that comes with the control of the monetary unit. I'm looking around here thinking about what would happen if instead of measuring wealth by tracking money earned, it was measured in terms of money given away. Right now, the richest 1,000 people in the world now hold as much wealth as the 3.5 trillion people on the other end of the spectrum combined. So what if there was a new measure of benefit to society. A tangible measure of debt forgiven and wealth given to the general populous. A measure of how far a person pushes themself to past the brink of reason to give it all away, similar to how deep a diver dares to swim or how high a climber dares to ascend.

Oh nevermind, that's just a bunch of nonscence. Here we are, halfway to Tuesday again. Already. Wow. Oh and how about that weather. Was it supposed to rain the other day? I don't know. Boy have I been busy with Thanksgiving right around the corner. Seems like it comes earlier and earlier every year, right? Did you watch that thing in the news yesterday? I don't know what the world is coming to. Well, there's a sale at Macy's so I better see if they have something I need. I better hurry, or I'll be late. Oh, wait till I tell you who I saw at church. Tell everyone I said hi.

It boggles my mind that all of that is normal conversation of the sane.

My folks think I'm out of my mind for coming out here. I think most of my old Pennsylvania people expect me to get myself jammed up in the nut house again. They probably picture me being held for ransom in some sort of POW style prison camp. I'm sure they're already expecting another phone call from me asking for sixty dollars bail money. I should have someone call that one in just as a joke. The last time we played that game it didn't go so well. I rotted to death for 5 weeks in one of America's fine criminal confinements for the crime of not having a ticket to be on a Greyhound bus. Well actually I did have a ticket, but when they dragged me off the bus kicking and screaming with pepper spray burning my eyes, my possessions ended up getting taken away. I got the ticket back after they let me out. It hangs framed on my wall as a reminder of days gone by.

Well, now the kiwi tells me that she was a high-class escort girl in New Zealand. No reason not to believe her. Might be true. She seems to believe it anyway. I guess I got a $2000 dollar ride for free. I think it's about time to part ways here. She's just too messed up. I have a feeling she's going to start blaming me for her problems. God, the fact that she holds it all together so well it's kind of scary.

She's strong in a way that tells me that she's gone down much harder, and survives much better than I've been capable of. The odds aren't in her favor though. Her people want her to go back to university. It sounds like there were tough times, then tougher, before she moved

23

from England to New Zealand. I feel bad for her. In a lot of ways I respect her but at the same time, I'm also repulsed by her. Quite a peach though, even if she does spread herself all around the map.

Our goodbye is an uneventful affair. It almost seems like she doesn't recognize me or remember me being around in the first place. She's headed north to the border, I'm going to stick around and explore Chang Mai for a couple more days I think.

Lord knows what the future brings her way. Don't give up on yourself, girl. Keep your moral compass true to your instincts and acquired wisdom. It seems difficult to love and be loved when those around you hurt and disappoint you. But there are others out there trapped in an impossible world feeling the same lonely frustrations. Oh the people you meet, the people you miss.

I decide to take a day to relax, do nothing, and just be an American idiot again. There's a boxing match I want to see today, Pacquiao vs Mayweather. The world's been waiting for these two champions to fight for 5 or 10 years. There's an Irish pub on the outskirts of Chang Mai that's showing the fight. The place is still serving brunch when I arrive, and there's a pretty fun group of ex-pats here to watch the fight also. Ex-pats are basically white guys from Europe and America in their 60's and 70's that have retired here because everything's so cheap. As the fight goes on they start joking with me about Thailand's prostitutes. I tell them I have no intention of taking part in that. They laugh and assure me that I would soon enough. I realize they're not kidding when they start talking about their "wives" and mistresses - girls in their teens and early 20's that they pay 5 or 10 dollars to have sex with whenever they feel like it. As they tell me where to find them I realize these innocent kids are everywhere. They go to school, work normal day jobs, and have meals with their families. But they also sell their bodies like a cheap commodity. It's a totally normal dynamic of the society here.

I'm deeply disturbed as our conversation goes on. The level of debauchery is out of control. The numbers and statistics and unsafe practices involved in this industry are disgusting. I get a sick feeling in my stomach, and for the rest of the day, as I wander around, I look at the population in a totally different way. I've read about the "flesh trade" here but seeing it first hand, and talking to these scum bags about it just makes me sad. The world is upside down, my head is spinning when I wander my way to a jazz bar on the northeast end of the city. The band is covering Led Zeppelin and Grateful Dead songs as well as I've ever heard. These kids are amazing, I mean these guys are seriously talented! I go up to the lead singer during a set-break to compliment him and realize that he barely speaks any English. I wonder if he even knew the meaning of the words he was just singing.

I'm exhausted when I get back to my room. I have trouble falling asleep processing the discovery that the majority of Thailand's fine ladies whore themselves around just as casually as my fair skinned love love bird. Every time I wake up to use the bathroom I'm nervous that it's going to burn when I pee.

I signed myself up for a "jungle trek" a couple days ago when I was still traveling with the kiwi. There are five other tourists on this expedition - younger guys from Canada. The guide picks us up just outside of town, and I gather that he's one of the few from his remote village that gets out that far. We're halfway to the middle of nowhere when he points to the horizon at our destination - his village. He's in his mid-20's, handsome chap and very personable. I ask him about his family and he says "I have nothing". That sticks with me - the way he said it. I have nothing either I guess.

There are no roads in the village, just paths beaten in the dirt by footsteps. They exchange no currency with each other but seem to have established some system of prices to charge tourists like me for things like water and snacks. It's an eye-opening experience, truly communal living. I wonder how some rinky dink agency in Bangkok got word all the way out here that a bloke like me would be showing up for this walkabout.

After a delicious meal of curry, vegetables, and the snake that one of the guys catches under the bungalow, we settle in for the night. But first, the children of the village gather around with the rest of the families and they sing songs for us in a bunch of different languages. I ask how they all know how to speak so fluently, and they say they learn it from folks like us traveling through their village all the time. It's incredible. There are chickens and pigs walking around happy all their lives till they become happy dinner, neighbors playing some hybrid game of kickball/volleyball in the dirt field. I'm sure their life is still tough in many ways, and that the older generations know this better than the younger ones, but today, right here, right now, everyone is happy. The world comes to them, then moves right along.

I'm ready for some beach in my life. From the pictures I've seen of the southern islands, it looks like a slice of paradise. Moving ahead at the speed of chaos I decide it's time to leave the region of culture and history behind, and go appreciate the ocean. I catch a tuk-tuk to the local airport and hop on a flight to the southern beaches for about the cost of a movie ticket back home. This economy here is so banged up it's silly.

Cities can be crowded, polluted, vulgar and full of scam artists and petty criminals. All things considered, Thailand's big cities are doing just fine though. Their civilization has evolved over several thousands of years of war, natural disasters, poverty and occupations by various monarchies and dictatorships. After all that, the infrastructure isn't too bad, economy is coming around, crime minimal, and the population is relatively happy and stress-free. Compare this to America. We've been in the civilization business for only about three hundred years, barely getting started. And we think we have all the answers. When our civilization breaks down it's usually from the inside out. The revolutionary war, the civil war, and more recent internal conflicts of wealth disparity and race relations. The French revolution was basically about wealth disparity. The rich and powerful can strike quick and fierce, but when the masses revolt it's often a bloody messy affair. Back then though you used to be able to find the Kings in their stone castles. It's not so simple anymore. The powers that be, the masters of our universe, are wandering around everywhere now. They tend to blend in better. We'll find you though when it's time to pay up.

My Lee

There seems to have been some sort of snafu in the mango stand / bus depot where I purchased my ticket for the 3-hour ride from Phuket to Krabi. My ticket is valid, but it appears that there are no available seats and no luggage storage. Adapt and overcome. I find an open spot by the back exit door where I can sit on the floor and lean on my pack. It's actually a nice vantage point, but I wish I had a cold beer. Nice colors on this bus. A proper pallet for a ride along the coast of the southern Thailand Bay. Blue window drapes with yellow, green, and red drapes over top. Nice fabric. The rain water leaking in from the ceiling doesn't detract from the pleasing aesthetics of the soft blue and red pleather panels. They're the type you would see on a kindergarten sofa, all solid colors. Apparently, the rain doesn't detract from the cozy nap that the guy in row 12 is taking either, his hoodie is soaked.

Well, all that Kiwi nonsense being in the past now, and having gained more than enough forward momentum for this trip, I think I should be able to settle in for a pleasant journey around this new island paradise I find myself in. Bangkok was the pits. I hadn't been that hot and disoriented since Bonnaroo. Good god, the heat and pollution almost put me down hard. Clearly, I was a tourist that couldn't tell up from down. But that's all yesterday's newspaper at this point. Hard to tell if any of it actually happened, or if it was just a lazy day dream.

And with that, she gets up and walks away, forever I assume. That dark cloud envelops me again. I thought it was just a feeling I had now and then years back before this episode of my life took hold. But now I remember, it's always here. It always has been and always will be. It was born at my conception and will live through to my death or beyond.

That bitch took my whole world with her. And now she passes it carelessly around. I look around this paradise of fools. These pretty girls bathing in the sun, the water, and the shade - whatever their choosing. And it is their choosing. This is their world, and all I can do is try to live in it. But the heat seems hotter, the air heavy, humid, the sweet smell of
28

her suntan lotion is gone, leaving only a stench of garbage and rotten
squid. Damn it, why does this always happen to me? I'm a nice guy,
smart, funny, interesting. I got my shit together for the most part – job
etc. I'm no Brad Pitt but I'm relatively attractive. It just doesn't make
sense.

And now she's gone. The money is gone. My brush with fame was a
passing daydream, gone. The kids, our friends, the only family I had left,
all gone. My confidence, my future, my hopes dreams and desires, all
gone. Gone, along with her beach towel and the book she was reading -
Paradise Lost.

Then I realize that the background noises of birds and crickets are gone.
The sound of the tide, gone. The water of this once peaceful cove, gone.
The sand underneath, gone exposing the sharp crag below.

Gone. It's all gone. You think you miss those things till they come flooding
back and engulf your world. I was down and out, but I wasn't delusional.
The ocean has receded a half mile into the horizon. I know right away
that as sure as day turns to night and winter to spring, this tide would
come back with the vengeance of hell. I run as fast as my feet have ever
taken me. Every stride I take is guided by my innate and deliberate
instinct to seek high ground. Unlike the cove I woke up on earlier this
morning, the flat land by this neighboring beach stretches back at least a
mile before it meets the bottom of the mountain pass. I fear it's an
impossible task, but I know that my best chance of survival is getting to
high ground before this wave comes in. If this tectonic event had
happened 20 minutes earlier I'd be arguing with her about this
impending tsunami. My panic would be trumped by her petty ignorance.

Ok, that's just a stupid story I started writing for no reason as I'm
watching these soft waves of warm water roll in and out. It's dripping
with symbolism and all that sort of crap. I wonder if I could be some
sort of professional writer someday. That's within the realm of
possibility, right? Nah, keep dreaming Montgomery.

I'm just happy to be on this beach right now. Such a change of scene from the ski season I just came from. My friend Kathryn from Vail told me to come here to Ton Sai because in the 6 months she spent traveling around South East Asia it was the best time she had. I decide to spoil myself and rent a private luxury beachfront bungalow for the whopping price of $15 a day. There's a string of five tavern huts leading down the dirt road from my place. Great fun.

About a half mile down along the beach there's a ladder leading up to a cool lookout over this cove, but if you keep hiking you cross over a ridge and end up in the neighboring beach town - Railay. This is the more built up part of the island. 5-star hotels, private swimming pools, markets, and fun tourist traps everywhere. The atmosphere is more like the beach towns I'm used to in America, but the natural beauty here will make your heart stop. It's surreal. Giant cliffs shooting straight up out of the emerald blue sea. White sand, and warm rolling water.

I'm on my way to get a cup of coffee to kill last night's hangover and start my day when I notice a sign for "Basecamp - Deep Water Soloing". Kathryn specifically mentioned this place and told me I had to do it. She also said to say hi to one of the guides named Suki.

The way this operation works is you basically boat out to one of the dozens of tiny islands jutting out of the sea, put on some worn out old climbing shoes, jump in the water, swim to the rock, and climb up. All the routes slope backward which makes them a bit of a challenge, but allows for climbing without a rope since when you fall you drop right into the water.

I meet a girl named Lee on the walk down the road from Basecamp to the shore. Lee the she. We sit across from each other on the boat ride and climb together all day. I can tell right away that something's going to happen between us. She's backpacking around the country just like I am without any real itinerary. She basically wandered into this day as unexpectedly as I did. We climb all day and party all night at those hut-taverns and end up back at my little bungalow. And just like that, I've traded in my Kiwi missy for a Jew princess.

Beautiful, smart, witty, genuine, young, sexy, playful, sensual, tender, mysterious. This is how I would describe her. She's reading one of my favorite books of all time - East of Eden. 25 - funny age. She wants to have a grown-up job. No longer satisfied with the life of a young waitress living abroad. She became a manager at her restaurant. That's just a headache I think. She's ready to move back to Miami from Israel where she's been living for the last seven years. She's always texting with her friends in Hebrew symbols, right-to-left. Talking in Hebrew with them on the phone - very guttural deliberate inflections.

So who is this pretty girl I have my arm around now? How did we come together like this? This sort of thing doesn't happen to me. I can't even remember the last time I got laid before Thailand, but now out here on this trip, I'm cavorting around like a regular ole Dan Juan.

What a wonderful beach game we came up with today - quite by accident I guess. We swam out in the water together, nuzzled up together and wouldn't you know it I happened to pop a giant boner. Oops. Must be the warm water and the exotic eyes of this sexual creature with her legs wrapped around my waist. Embarrassing?... not really. We kind of look around - not too crowded out here, so we kind of wiggle ourselves together, and just like that we're having sex in the ocean. I wonder how many other people have played this game and I've never noticed. Great fun.

So we go exploring different beaches, getting in and out of the water all day and playing our new game. Considering how surreal it is just to be in a tropical island setting like this, it was just plain magical to be slowly boning out there all day. Funny. Besides that we are just chillin like homies, be-bopping around the island, living it up like the rich and fancy lovers of this world do.

It really is something special though - this place, this girl. We get out of the water around sunset and a woman tells us that she snapped a couple pictures of us because we looked so happy and in love out there. She asked if we had just gotten married. Of course, I say yes, and

31

my Lee plays right along.

Three days we've been together now. It seems like three years. There's no real certainty of a future between two people whether they've known each other as companions, lovers, or even family. Moments matter. Memories matter. But what this lacks in future certainty it certainly makes up for in moments lived fully in the present and times that will live on as unforgettable scenes in the past.

Here we exist now in our tumbleweed lives. I think we both sort of wonder what future will catch us, who we'll share it with, and where we'll go. Whatever happens in the future we can always maybe think of each other and the bond we shared. This trip together will be a good waypoint to help navigate what direction we take forward and where we want to be. For now, our waypoint is north to Ko Phangan on this super speed boat catamaran ferry. What awaits us there? Apparently, they go crazy for some sort of full moon party every month. Drugs, fire, techno music, naked hippies acting like lunatics. Sounds like a real hoedown, but I'm happy to be arriving between cycles. I think I'm getting too old for shit like that.

I got lucky here. Everything random is falling into place and moving forward like the wind. Luck happens, but not by random chance alone. Sure, the spark of our chance meeting couldn't have been arranged, but the openness to drive our lives in a direction that allowed the magical setting of these last few days to be possible has been an active effort on both our parts. Efforts with no end result in mind. And it wasn't blind luck that brought our lips together while spinning on that hanging chair for a magical movie-like first kiss. Motorbiking around the islands, chasing monkeys, poaching million dollar swimming pools, drinking whiskey and singing Gaelic folk songs with some old guy from Ireland and his little Thai mistress - magical.

Things that don't exactly turn me on about this Lee - sometimes the formal way she casually dresses, like the artsy aunt that shows up to the family reunion. Her sexual honesty - I just don't need to know that even though you're not a slut you've been able to explore and find yourself sexually. I don't know, maybe on second thought, I love all that. Her eyes are intoxicating, and her lips are full. I correctly guessed that she has Arabic roots while we were chit-chatting about this and that in one of our ocean roustabouts. She lights up the scene like a Disney Princess character. She gets me going. Whenever we touch, I'm immediately aroused. That's rarely ever happened with other girls. And yeah, she's funny, but not overtly, and not with any real effort or intention like me - the comedian, the sad clown. She'll say things that'll make me honestly stop, chuckle, and shake my head. Nice gal. Luckily I'm not in love with her.

Blow Holes

"We?" she asks. A more powerful and provocative question has not been asked since the dawn of mankind. And there she lays wanton and befuddled by a feeling of vulnerability that she cannot suppress. But it's a comfortable state of mind for her. It's better to be lost then found. To accept a seeker that has found her would mean she'd have to stop hiding, stop running. Children stop running and hiding when they're bored of playing hide and seek, or when their parents tell them to come in for supper.

Kids of this porn generation don't need to go in for supper. Their supper is everywhere. With easy access to the stimulation and information that my generation had to wait patiently for, the porn generation need not abide by any law or incentive. But the generation before them will still invest in the promise of higher education even though it can only regiment a course of study. The knowledge that used to only be available to those privileged enough to purchase a ticket to university is now readily available to anyone with the interest. A diploma is no longer worth the cost of a house. In a similar fashion, sex is no longer worth the cost of a house. It seems to me that lately there's more trust and compassion between friends then there is between lovers.

It used to be impossible to routinely see a girl's eyes when you and she embraced, except for the lucky ones who found their way to a stable passionate marriage with lots of kids. Now, to scratch that carnal itch a person need only turn on their computer, vibrator, or pocket phone and pull the trigger on a shot of ecstasy. She doesn't need the promise of a house and garden anymore. And he no longer needs to prove his worth and commitment. The paradigm is rapidly fading.

The heat is getting hotter here, but the natives in these island towns don't seem to mind. I, on the other hand, have to take refuge in the air condition every time I see a 7-11. For some reason, this convenience store franchise has a huge footprint in Thailand. The night times are

34

always nice and cool though. We've been having a lovely time scootering around between tiki pubs and street markets once the sun goes down.

We seem to have picked back up with this obnoxious English woman again when we get off the boat from Ko Phangan to Ko Tao. She was hanging around with us a week ago in Ton Sai. Don't get me wrong, she's a hoot, but I'm not exactly thrilled that she seems to be cunt-blocking my Lee away from me.

We're all hanging out having a few drinks after arriving in Ko Tao when I go around the block secure a room for my Lee and myself. But when I get back to the bar Lee tells me she's thinking she wants to stay in the dorm hostel with Kay and get back on her original path of backpacking solo. Was it something I said? Sure, we only met a couple days ago, but I'd never ditch a lover like that. Maybe it was because we got into a heated discussion of Israel's place in geopolitical affairs a couple nights earlier that started to turn her off. I don't know. I guess it's an easy enough let down all things considered. I'm just too prone to get attached and wrapped up in the possibility of a future with someone. This cycle has gone on for so long and has become so predictable. It's frustrating and disheartening.

Are gender roles completely shifted? Isn't this feeling usually more often associated with girls getting used and tossed aside by the fellas? Am I just a mess under the cool put together image I project? Maybe I don't project that at all. Maybe when their attention shifts from their first impression of my steely blue eyes to my awkwardly big nose they become disenchanted. Maybe my unique outlook on life goes from being alluring to alarming. I don't know, and I only have like a hundred more years to figure it out.

Too bad, I liked that girl, and more than just the way a puppy likes his thrusts object. But maybe that's all she wanted - a little slam piece to fit into her vacation. She and Kay are still staying by the dock. I've moved to the northern part of the island to start dive school. I love it. I

35

was chillin underwater for 45 minutes today. I'm taking a 4-day / 4-night scuba training course. It's pretty interesting learning about buoyancy, the body's reaction to pressure, nitrogen in the blood, and self-contained underwater breathing apparatus.

I've taken Nitrogen for granted for so long. It's everywhere, I had no idea. Apparently, it makes up 78% of our atmosphere. It's inert - doesn't really do anything, like me, so everyone takes it for granted I guess. As best I can gather from the videos we watched in class today it seems to just sort of come and go in the blood. But like carbon dioxide or oxygen, if there's too much hanging around and the ambient pressure drops it'll sort of settle out of solution and coagulate in your body. If it doesn't get processed you basically get drunk under water.

You also have to be mindful of constant breathing and not surfacing too fast or else you could get the dreaded "bends". Your lungs could explode and your eyeballs could pop out of your head into your goggles if the pressure gets fucked up. At about 12 meters deep or so, the pressure is twice that of our air. What happens with "the bends" is that if you breathe in a big puff of air, then surface immediately, your lungs will pop. Think of a balloon that's filled all the way up, then the pressure around the balloon is minimized. The balloon will expand and pop. It's important to know all these things, and completely ignore them at the same time because panic is the worst thing that can happen. If your breathing rate gets too quick, your buoyancy gets all out of whack, and you get too distracted to catch a ride on the whale shark that just swam by. That's basically how scuba works.

I start day dreaming when our instructional video gets talking about embolisms. I think you have a stroke or something because nitrogen bubbles are smaller than something. Blah blah blah, who cares? Let's get down there like Jacques Cousteau and look at some fish.

I guess this thing with Lee pisses me off, but I'll tell you what really grinds my gears right now - fucking blow holes! These fish, huge fish, they spend their entire lives underwater but can't breathe down there so they suck wind from the surface when nobody is looking. Sharks, tuna, urchins, all making an honest living completely under the sea, then you got these guys half full of air, lumbering around all day and moaning for the entire god damn ocean to hear, and I bet nobody knows they have a fucking blow hole on their back. People give them a free pass by saying they're mammals - fuck that. They're fish, idiots.

Our instructor Claus is a complete lunatic, I love it. He's like 60 years old with a 5-year-old son that straps on a tank and follows us underwater like a puppy dog. We're throwing back cold beers all night after our first day of open water dives when he tells us he's hoping that someone is hungover enough to throw up under water. Apparently when that happens fish come swimming from everywhere to feast on the nutrient-rich vomit. Sounds glorious.

My fellow classmates are a hoot as well - three German chaps and one 18-year-old kid from Holland. He's like a parody of a kid from Holland - a baker, like a Muppet cartoon. He got laid on the beach last night but he said that "his ding dong stopped working". One of the Germans fellas got laid that night too but it was by a Thai girl, no condom. He said her brother watched and filmed it. I don't know what to make of that story. This is a silly place.

Okay, well now that Lee's gone there are thoughts that need to be processed. Our time was like a tsunami in reverse. She came in and flooded my world unexpectedly. It was a day. Wow. It was 24 hours of... I don't even know what to call it. It was just fun. Basically, it was just more fun than I have ever had in a 24 hour period. And it was passionate and magical, but not the passion you have with a lover necessarily. Or maybe it was. It was like it was a movie, and then the director said cut.

Now that the wave of the tsunami is receding to the abyss of the ocean I have to prepare for the wake it will leave behind. The exposed crag of the seabed, the rotten squid, and then as sure as sunrise follows sunset, the ecstasy of falling asleep with her in my arms will sour my dreams and make my next few mornings feel empty and meaningless.

37

So yeah, I have to watch out for those dark feelings. They're not real. Well, they are, but knowing where they're coming from might help me come down from this high.

It's funny how similar the parting of ways was with the young Jewess and the even younger Kiwi. In the end, which came shortly after their beginnings, they wanted to go on their own because that was the original intent of their trip. They both said that they didn't want the "story of the trip" to be the meeting and romance of a stranger. But they both said it was lots of fun, no regrets. Neither had too deep of an emotional attachment, especially the Kiwi. But she was in a unique situation in that she was a professional.

I've heard it said that girls don't marry the men they love, as much as marry the guy they're with when they decide they're ready to settle down. Like it's about timing, not meaning. Cycles. They cycle with the tides.

I'm walking around reflecting on these things when who do I see across the street - my Lee. It's funny, I was just thinking of sending her a message to see if she wants to get dinner. We hang out for a couple hours chumming around the island but go our separate ways after the sun goes down. I've lost interest. Why do I always come back to the same conclusion? Emotional self-defense probably. Their interest in me always fades. I say - fuck it because I'm disappointed in their taste in men. I'm pretty sure that in the big picture, I'm a gem. Time and time again I'm passed over by gals that shop their interests around somewhere else after a fling with me. If I were her I wouldn't have left the person whose company I was enjoying in order to go hang out with Kay. There's clearly something I'm just not seeing here. Why won't someone just shoot me straight one of these times?

This Jew princess flooded my world with a physical love I haven't felt in... ever maybe. She's adventurous and intellectual, not as much emotional though. I guess that's all for the best out here. Most likely she'll go her way and I'll go mine and that'll be that. Maybe though, there's a chance that we realize we both miss what we had. But this will never happen again - this love in paradise thing. I guess it wasn't love anyway, just a chance coming together of two passionate souls. One year. Let's circle back to this one in a year. I'm going to be tempted to invite her to Vail. Maybe next spring. I'll invite her to Vail next spring.

The novelty of her company has worn off anyway. She annoys me. Without her around things are back in balance. I don't have to mope around and dwell on having been rejected. I can honestly feel an equal partner in this progression. Nice gal.

She said she hopes she's not pregnant. I'm sure she's not because the only times I let myself go was when my dong-bag was firmly in place. But I was inside of her for hours in the ocean. Sometimes nature says okay, let's make a move on this one. Whatever. I'd be totally fine with having a love child. I'd name it Love Child Montgomery and encourage it to... to... whatever; I guess follow its hopes and dreams to the depths of hell and back just like old Pappy.

Murky Mire

This heat is killing me. I believe it's time to start planning my trip home. There are plenty of cheap flights out of Bangkok. As much as I don't want to go back to that place it seems like that's what's going to have to happen. The German chaps are headed that way next, so hanging with them for a couple more days should be a fun way to cap off this adventure.

I know that on these types of journeys, looking back, I'll see that I was maybe in some risky situations that I didn't realize were dangerous at the time. As we arrive back in Bangkok I realize that my first day in this country a month ago was that time. It's dirty and crowded and the locals prey on the tourists that are clearly lost. I don't trust them. I feel lucky to have stayed safe and out of trouble. Even though I did some things that would be too risky for some people, my guard was always up. I stayed aware and usually felt in control of the situation. Take it minute by minute, try to make good decisions, roll with the punches, trust your instincts.

I make a temporary new companion on my plane ride home - another young beauty named Merris. She's returning back to the States after teaching English in a Chinese village for the last two years. Intelligent, cute, skinny, brunette, 25 years old. Fun to talk to. How might I describe her personality?... like the middle child of an 80's sitcom, although I think she just has one younger brother. I hope to be able to follow her story a bit on the Facebook. I think that assimilating back to "Western civilization" will be an interesting thing for her.

Gathering momentum into the unknown is a challenge sometimes, but coming back to reality is a whole other animal indeed. Reentry has been much more difficult than I anticipated. Instead of gliding into my home port I hit a jagged quagmire. After an exhausting two-day journey back through LA to Denver, I find myself locked out of my friend Reuben's condo where I was planning to sleep the night and the next day. It's 1 am and I'm exhausted. I walk over to his local pub but the bartender tells me he just left. She thinks he's at the next pub down the street. He's not there either. Once again I'm exhausted, I have no local currency, no batteries left on my cell phone, probably smell terrible, and I'm hauling around a backpack full of bullshit. The bar is closing up and I'm pretty much all out of options.

I'm telling my sad story to the drunk girl next to me at the bar. Turns out she knows Reuben and isn't surprised he forgot I was coming because he was shit faced all night. She invites me back to her place where she and her five roommates have an all-night cocaine and 80's music dance party. I immediately pass out on the sofa in the back of the room but drift in and out of consciousness just enough to appreciate my good fortune and flashbacks to my younger years when these songs were new and popular.

I check my voice mail after being back in cell service range for the first time in a month. Brother Vin left me a curious sounding message weeks ago right after I left for Asia. We haven't talked in quite some time, but it's always nice catching up. I tell him about my trip, and we talk about life in general, then he tells me he has some news. Ok, let's hear it. His dad died... like a month ago, right after I left for Asia... What?!? I don't even know what to say. I express disbelief and condolence. Vin starts giving me some of the details, but I'm numb, mute; in a state of shock maybe. I don't know what to do now. I need to step outside.

Fannie, one of my domestic life partners, sees me for the first time in a month as I'm walking out the door. Welcome back how was the trip, she says. I can't even speak. I just need to walk away and process this.

Don was quite possibly the most influential person in my life, in that he was the bane of my existence. I have no words and no thoughts as I walk. The Colorado air is crisp and cool as I remember it. I'm passively noticing things that I've walked right past a million times or more. That's to be expected after coming back from such a transformative trip I guess. But I don't care about these observations right now. I look right past them up at the stars, around at the mountains, at the street signs and cars along the street. Everything is just as it was an hour ago, but this entire world seems completely different to me now. There is nothing in my head - it's just still, quiet. Is this real? Wow. This can't be real.

Back at home, I tell Fannie the news, and she's in a state of disbelief as well. She knows all about the scarring memories and issues I carry with me from the past. I had to cut him out of my life a few years ago after coming to the realization that I'd never be able to stop fixating on the abusive things he did and said for all those years. Nothing but negative words – not just to me, but also against me in the very impressionable ears of ma. He'd parade around for everyone to admire as this corporate hot shot, holier-than-thou Catholic show off, then come home and rip me apart day after day - year after year. What is it with people like that using religion to hide their true selves?

When confronted with undeniable wrongs like physical abuse, ma once told me "it was provoked anger that I'm sure he regrets". Really? Did you ever regret it, Don? Did you ever tell her that you regret the way you treated me? I doubt it, but that's what she's allowed herself to believe, and that's the tide of denial I've had to swim upstream against my entire life. How would you like it if someone was putting all sorts of garbage about you in your mom's ear for your entire life?

I'd never be able to prove it without ma admitting it, but I'm certain it was his idea to throw me in the nut house that very first time. It was on the day of my return from my failed attempt at becoming a naval officer. On that day, when they tricked me into going to the hospital I immediately deteriorated from a newly graduated young man with a world of potential to a bitter insane raging bull. From that point forward, his decades of slander were legitimized. That day, that terrible day changed my life. In the first hour of being locked up, I went from annoyed, to confused, to angry, to fucking bat shit crazy. After half a day of waiting for an explanation of why I'm being so jammed up I had my first experience of being wrestled to the ground by three of the hospital staff and injected with some drug that immediately turned me into a brain dead vegetable. Was I insane, or was I justifiably raging about being so blindsided and mistreated? Within a month, the toxic level of lithium I was being fed turned me into a pathetic tranquilized zombie barely able to function. That was the new starting point from which I had to make my way in this world. How did shit go so sideways so quickly? Maybe in the month I was away I lost my mind and they were justified sending me to the funny farm. Maybe the real mistake was letting me out - an act of provoked mercy that I'm sure they regret...

I just can't believe he's dead. What in the hell happened? According to Vin, it was a sudden reaction to a relatively mild drug he was recently prescribed. Wait a minute, according to his obituary he died a couple days before I left for Asia. I talked to ma twice between the time he died and the day of the funeral, and all she had to say was that she didn't support my decision to travel to such a dangerous part of the world.

Part of his write up in the newspaper says:

"His generosity led him to become a Knight Commander in the Equestrian order of the Holy Sepulchre of Jerusalem dedicated to the preservation and propagation of the Catholic faith in the Holy Land"

So it looks like Don has passed into the ether, and is heralded as practically a saint in his circle of friends, colleagues, clergy and family - most of whom spend their entire lives looking for the embodiment of a savior. Singing together about grace and faith and God and the golden rosary of hosts or something like that. He embodied everything I perceive as evil in this world. But he's a Knight Commander now and I just have to accept that. The Association of Equestrian Princes of the Spectrum of Light or whatever bullshit association he rose to the top of would probably have me hung and quartered if they ever heard me speaking ill of him. What is this group, some fancy order of the Catholic Church that has to make a big deal about themselves so that everyone knows they're a couple steps higher than the rest of the parishioners that go their churches every Sunday? Mom will probably be on display saying more prayers than ever at his ghost and the higher council of dead spirits. Then she'll come home, turn on Fox News and hate on

43

poor people for being lazy. I used to have an imaginary friend named Jesus. I had to leave him back at the nut house for practical reasons. Maybe I should send him a postcard. Maybe I should send ma a postcard. Maybe a phone call would be more appropriate. She knows I hated the guy though. How does a person go about making amends with a maternal ghost widow?

As it turns out, nothing of significance ever happened between me and Don. Everybody knows it, haven't you heard? It's just the way it is was and always will be. It's just best that I get behind that story and move on. I think I can box it up and put it away in a quiet little shadow of a wooded brook that barely gets walked past anyway. I've told people about it, but it's best that they forget it too. Just a little patch of thorns and poison ivy that the kids would do best to stay away from anyway. There is a golden road 4 times over the horizon. Tales of peace and goodness leading to light and wisdom. No need for further exploration of a murky mire. No fish in that mud. No worms even for the birds to choke on. Pine cones can sit there but not take. Sand and stones and rocks underneath can stay buried there as they were destined to. The world will keep spinning; floods, droughts, and famine will surely come and go as is the nature of things. But for the most part, that little grove should stay untouched by the footprints of man. Which is nice. There's not a lot of places like that left out there. To have known that such a place existed at one point is kind of neat I guess. Once forgotten though it would just sit back in a soft and aging mind to maybe be mixed in with the tales of castles and dragons whispered to the kids around the campfire. Legend, fable, mysterious garden - it's funny the way these things take root and grow. What was I talking about? Well, I should go. It's almost dinner time and it looks like it's starting to rain anyway.

2

A Paradigm Shift of the Zeitgeist

The Knightman cometh

My settling back into normalcy hasn't been super smooth, but I think I'm back to myself again. In order to hold on to my sanity, it's essential for me to get good sleep, and that just hasn't happened for a while. Well, there was one day when I slept from like 10 a.m. till about 7 p.m. That was needed, but it sent my jet lag adjustment back a couple steps. Mostly I've been sleeping for about 5 hours, then waking for about 5 or 10. Day or night is irrelevant. When I wake up it takes me a while to realize where I am. My dreams keep putting me right back on the beach, so when I roll over in bed I'm sure I'm in one of the 20 Thailand bungalows I stayed in over there. So that's a lot of fun. Going to sleep is fun too. It's often late morning or early afternoon after eating when I pass out exhausted in my comfortable bed.

I express in a letter to ma my sorrow for her loss and understanding of their love even though he and I had our differences. I reference some fonder memories of him from when I was about 5, and I say how close I've always felt to all of Don's family members, especially his dad. We've had a strained relationship the last few years and I tell her that if ever there is a time for her and me to just leave the past in the past, this is it.

I haven't talked to brother Rich, but Vin and Joe seem to be dealing with the situation just fine. They say mom is handling everything with no problem as well. It's funny, for at least the last month, every day has

45

been so random. I've woken up every morning knowing that by the end of the day unpredictable things were going to happen; like ending up in a different ocean, or meeting a new stranger and taking off in a random direction. Scuba diving and rock climbing happened unexpectedly. I woke up not knowing that those types of things were going to happen each day, and I have grown used to that. So this thing with Don follows right along with that in a sense. I didn't see it coming, but I'm not really in too much disbelief about it I guess.

I guess I'll go back to Brixton soon to sort of pay my respects or something like that. It's weird, I feel like a normal person that would go back to his hometown now. It feels like there was some force field that kept me from the place that isn't there anymore. I think I envisioned that as part of Don's death. For sure I did.

I'm thinking about how my role in the family has dramatically shifted. For one thing, I now consider myself part of the family again. Secondly, I'm sort of a patriarch of the family there. Oldest brother by ten years, close with all the other brothers and looked up to by them for sure. There's no anger for the dead now. Who cares. It's nice to know he won't be around to piss me off when I go back. And that's really all that matters. He was basically just annoying; the way a school bully treats you like a bitch and makes you just want to avoid him.

I don't exactly know how the others felt about their dad, and it doesn't really matter I guess. Well, I think Vin and his dad had a good relationship. Rich used to yell and scream bloody murder at his dad all the time - like daily - for a decade. I don't really have any idea what their relationship was like in the more recent years.

The somewhat normal schedule I've fallen into is early to bed, early to rise. It's nice as long as you do it because you're tired, not because you need to wake up early for work. I can't believe I lived like that for so long. Thank god I told my old boss to fuck off way back when. It was a rough transition at first, but I wouldn't have been able to live this kind of life if I didn't snap that day. It was liberating. I think everyone should drop the hammer on an authority figure at least once in their life. I think I did the guy that took my place a favor too. It was a good deed and everyone involved is better off I think. I hope more people pay it forward like that. Tell 'em to fuck off and then sing a bar of Alice's Restaurant. Getting up early to hustle to a job where you're not appreciated sucks. And too many of us do it. It all comes back to some sort of human instinct that perpetuates this mysterious dynamic that feeds the beast his power.

Have I told you that I recently sold the world for just under fourteen dollars and 72 cents? I live on the 6th floor of a high-rise now. It's quite fashionable.

Have I told you that the stars come out at night when sister is away? She brought a bear to the reunion last week. It was quite fashionable.

Have I told you about the weeping willow? It was struck by lightning while everyone was asleep in the pantry. A likely story I suppose.

Did you know that just over half of my record collection was stolen and turned into scrap metal and paper mache? It illuminated my mind and was quite fashionable

That's a little poem I just wrote because god put it in my head. Instead of a rhyme scheme, it uses a phrase scheme. It's a new thing - quite fashionable. I give brother Joe a call to see how things are going these days. I ask him why I haven't heard from Rich in so long. Is he avoiding me for some reason? Joe tells me that Rich is literally prepared to kill me if I come around. Wait... what??? He tells me that Rich sees me as a threat to the family. He says Rich told him that if I come around everyone needs to be ready to act to protect mom. He tells me that Rich says he "is ready to lay down his life to protect mom from me".

So this is what I have to deal with in my life right now. Fuck it. Apparently, as they were all discussing how to not tell me Don died, they were preparing plans to deal with me if I came back to Brixton. Now that I think about it I remember my good friend Ivan mentioning something about this. But he was in or the ruse too. He lives just on the other side of Brixton, and we emailed back and forth a couple times while I was in Thailand.

It's a shame, we used to be tight. I was one of the few friends he had and we helped each other through some tough times in life. I was at his place last year when he lived in Denver. It was obvious that he drank whiskey, smoked pot, watched movies, ate Twinkies and played video games till 4 in the morning every day. He was almost 30 years old and taking about 8 credits per semester of art classes. But still, he would always talk about how busy he is, just like ma who hasn't had a job in 25 years. And like her, all his life expenses and obligations were completely paid for by the Knight Commander. Helpless like a rich man's child. He kind of reminds me of Ignatius Reilly or the comic book guy from The Simpsons.

Joe tells me that the family gathered around in mom's room the morning of the funeral to discuss the do's and don'ts of talking to me. Ironically they were saying that I might play mind games and get info from them by pretending I don't know certain things. Ironically, I would never have to do that if they would be straight with me and treat me like a normal person. I can't help it if I've developed enough intuition to detect when people lie to me. Once you're got, you're got, and I'll take your whole chip stack when I catch your tell; and your neighbor's too. Fuckers.

Has everyone completely lost their goddamn mind? Clearly, the crazy one here is fratricidal maniac trying to, I don't know, to justify his life now by playing the role of some sort of martyr. Idiot. Joey tells me he goes to church now and says the rosary all the time. That's hilarious because he's always been as cynical about religion as anyone.

"I am happy if I must die. This is because I am a Catholic and I know that what is in store for me is eternal life with Our Father inside the kingdom of heaven. No other philosophy or so-called religion offers such a deal: participate in the liturgy of the Church, accept an offer of love from God
48

in the form of Holy Eucharist, proclaim the teachings of His Son Jesus Christ, die in a state of grace, and know that what awaits you is divine love and happiness for the rest of eternity. Nice deal - works for me."

An excerpt from the note mom sent back to me in response to my condolence. He seems more at peace than I probably will on my death day. Maybe there's a lesson there. I wonder if the Knight Commanders of 500 years ago felt at peace at the hour of their deaths on the battlefields of the Crusades.

They were so "dedicated to the preservation and propagation of the Catholic faith in the Holy Land" that they gave their lives and took the lives of the infidels. How proud they and their families must have been in their righteous slaughter for such a pure and noble cause.

His last chapter, his last verse. I'm sure he believed that "Nice Deal" will be written in gold and transcribed by the holiest of scholars… and he may be right. Maybe I'm the only person on this earth that saw him as an asshole. I guess I represented basically his only sign of imperfection; the bastard child treated as such; a footnote to his legacy. It's easily overlooked though because I'm the bitter insane fool touched by the devil himself as evidenced by the madness witnessed while incarcerated and institutionalized.

Well, this is my gospel, my testament - the first letter of Madman to the Equestrians. Scattered half thoughts ripe with quotes that could be taken in or out of context as just cause for an indictment of lost sanity and moral decay punishable by a life of inpatient and outpatient solitude and an afterlife of eternal hellfire. I despair my desperate disparity from the parity of the clergy's clarity. So these I suppose are my words and thoughts. I'm a monster it seems. As he would say "how can I even look at myself in the mirror?" I will tell you if you'd like to know - I open my eyes in my reflection's direction and contemplate my existence.

How is it that Catholicism is the only truth, and other "so-called religions" are blasphemy? How do intelligent people convince themselves to look past the history of some of the bloodiest campaigns that man has ever fought against fellow man in the name of this "so called religion"? These beliefs will always defy logic, that's just the way it is. He can die with this belief in a hospital with the blessings of priests, bishops, and liturgy all literally drinking from the same cup of what they convince themselves is the blood of Christ. I'll be over here breathing what I have convinced myself is fresh air. Newsflash, drinking blood is gross.

I visited Don's office back when I was in college once. I had applied for an internship and was eager to learn about the pharmaceutical industry. I remember very distinctly him showing me some of the newest artwork being done in his marketing department for bipolar medication. It's a bit fuzzy because it was so long ago, but I remember a picture of a face or a head, half red, half blue; obviously representing the manic and depressive states.

He knew all about the moves his company was making to cash in once a doctor gave you the diagnosis of bipolar. It's incurable by definition, so a person will need to purchase a lifetime worth of expensive pills or else risk another spiral brought on by withdraw from their poison. If his company didn't corner the market, the rivals would.

He knew the pharmaceutical dynamics of this disease better than anyone when he and mom had me forcibly committed. He knew what the aftermath would be. It's scary how such an action taken by nonprofessionals such as parents can fuck a person's life right up. A label of bipolar is by definition irreversible and incurable. And all it takes is one doctor watching you rage against your involuntary admission to the psyche ward to apply that death sentence. That level of severity is enough to block a person from getting affordable healthcare for the rest of their lives. Whether his actions were taken to fuck me over or not, the system is rigged, and it sucks. He knew it, and he profited by it. The amount of prayers a person must have to mutter to themselves in order to quell their cognitive dissonance and prop up their self-righteous ego must be astronomical. And the more you say, the more you can convince yourself that you're going to heaven anyway, so keep doing the master's bidding.

Mom told me once a couple years ago that they say novenas at some weekly gathering. She didn't tell me as much as she bragged about it. Novenas are when you say the rosary 9 times. The rosary is when you say the Hail Mary 60 times sprinkled with a couple Our Fathers, Holy Ghosts, and an Apostles Creed. It seems to me to be a competition of vanity when you put it on display like that. I just don't see any creativity, soul searching or actual meditation in mumbling these words to yourself or in a group over and over. I don't know, maybe it helps some people cope with their guilt, despair or confusion.

It's too bad they changed the name of the condition from manic-depressive to Bipolar, because Jimi Hendrix had a beautiful song about the condition that could become lost on my brothers and sisters riding this wave. But that's marketing for you. Nice Deal.

At one point Don and ma had me going to the same psychiatrist as brother Rich. Having met with Don, Rich, and ma, his assessment was that Don was the textbook definition of a narcissist and that ma was an enabler living in denial. Even in the later years when I would try to leave it all in the past, Don would find a way to blindside me. Our final interaction that ended our relationship for good came 5 years ago as brother Joe was a senior in high school looking at colleges to enroll in. I planned for months to take a trip home from Colorado to bring him to a Penn State football game. It was a trip mom fully supported and even encouraged, and that Joe was very much looking forward to. At the last minute, Don derailed the idea saying that he didn't "want to put Joe's future at risk". Actually, he had mom deliver the news. Joe and I were both dumbfounded. I knew that if I didn't end our relationship right there and then, I might find myself in jail someday because nobody would be there to defend me if I acted on provoked anger like he did.

"All happy families are alike; each unhappy family is unhappy in its own way." Leo Tolstoy said that. "I'll let you be in my dreams if I can be in yours." Bob Dylan said that.

Train mood forest mood.

I'm dying a death. It doesn't feel great. And it lingers now. I should be ok I guess. Things are pretty good I guess. Job is fine, money is there if I need it. People... they all think I'm an idiot... but there are people around that know me, and I guess that's nice.

Fuck me, man. Yeah, I talked to mom today, and after a while, I mentioned that I was thinking of coming home this fall, but that I have heard from a couple sources that Rich has been saying some pretty aggressive things about me. Mom said she can't talk about that now. She probably thinks the phone is tapped. Fuck it. Who cares what a person's mom thinks about them. The devil, that's who. Nah, a mom is just a person anyway. Some people are just born to the wrong parents. Bob Dylan said that once, and I think there's a lot of truth to it. I don't know. Who knows.

Man, I thought that was all over. I thought that was in the past. I thought that was gone. The world felt different when I found out Don was dead. I felt like I could go "home" again. Now, it feels worse; like there's a new dark force there. I finally felt like it was an ok time to go back to dumb ole Brixton and not feel threatened in any way. I've been talking to parents, grandparents, and brothers more than I used to, and I've really been trying to make an effort to stay in touch with people in the fam. I hadn't been doing that for a while.

There are a couple other things going on in my life that would be of note if I wasn't being crushed to my core by these things. I shouldn't be after all this time, but I am. I had let it go, man. It was gone, it was written off, it was all moot, a moot point. And now it just still is, and now it becomes apparent that it always will be. And that is a very deflating reality to come upon. It always will be whether I'm here for five more minutes, five more years or 55 more years. This is just the burden I have to live with and it's the god damn twisted truth.

It's a fucked up twisted existence, and those with good sense stay blind to the reality of the dying world that we live in. Damn. Maybe I'm so fucked up that I can't just enjoy the beauty of life. It's all around. I enjoy it, but I'm sure it's just about a heartbeat away from rotting to waste. Maybe I just need to go away. Maybe just disappear. I was thinking that this off-season I'd fly "home" for a bit, then to Rome. But why would I go back to a place I'm not wanted. Why would I stay? I don't know. I don't care.

I hurt real bad. I was having one of those moments earlier that I just had to choke down. I needed to just bury my head in my knees and die... just stop breathing for a while and just suffer and hurt it out for a bit, but I was at work, so I had to let it cook boil and fester for a few hours. I'm sort of numb now, but will need to fully suffer that thing real soon I'm sure. I just hate my life sometimes, man. I just hate it, and I shouldn't. I'm so weak it's pathetic. And I recognize how pathetic that is, and that makes it even worse. If I were anyone else looking at this I'd spit on me, puke on me, hate at me, flick old crusty tears at me.

I hurt man, I really hurt. Maybe that's what he wants. I really thought that was all over man. I thought there was a new fucking chapter in this life man. I thought I was going to be able to... rehabilitate. But his parasite lives on and continues to feed off the host body that was my mom. I have a weak mind that is easily broken. Like a shoulder that pops out of its socket, and each time it does is more weakened and more likely to go again. Like an allergy to peanuts or mushrooms or bee stings. You would think a tolerance would build up naturally, but the opposite happens. Each occurrence of these afflictions is worse than the last.

My life and all my love is in vain and that's only the tip of the iceberg. Surrounded by all this beauty and happiness, all my love is in vain. What very little of this love I have left to give and to get squashed is all in vain I'm afraid, and I just don't see what point there is to keep trying. I hate myself and all my love is in vain. But I'll carry on I'm sure. No need to call the karma police at this time. I don't know, I just don't know.

train mood, forest mood

ugh. [and then he slept the sleep of angels]
53

A family conspires against itself. A brother lives openly with homicidal intentions toward another brother. The lifelong friend is paralyzed with self-pity. The earth turns, the tide goes out, the moon runs around the planet, a bird dives to the bottom of the lake - his kin watch. Dawn comes. Again. Dusk, dawn, another dusk. Kings are crowned, heads are chopped off. Opinions are formed out of the moldy cheese. Frustration festers for the enlightened humblemen burning at the stake. Shit melts into the gutter. She licks it up and the suitors follow in droves. The moon phases to the crescent. An innovation threatens to save humanity from ignorance and is quickly lashed by illogic to the pleasure of the masses. But in a corner of the angry mob stands an idiot. He bashes his head on the steel bars of the armory. Nobody cares. Why should they? Tide comes in. Dusk gives way to another new dawn. The omen of mist causes a river of blood. Who is to blame? How has the idiot caused such turmoil from his small box? Burn him. Crucify him. He is the root of all evil and shall be shunned for eternity or longer - until he learns that he is... nothing. Nothing will set you free. Nothing. Believe in nothing. You are nothing.

Haiku to Golgi

Tree roots, tentacles
Bloom upside-down inside out
A mirror image

Like birds of the sky
Worms dive to earth's nickel core
Great Tree parallel

I have written this two framed Haiku for Golgi. I'm considering worshiping the Golgi apparatus instead of the Great Tree. I mean I guess trees are amoebas anyway so it's basically the same thing. Life flows inside and outside of us all, whether we are single-celled or otherwise.

The earth stokes it nuclear flame with minerals and whatnot from this intermediate surface we live on. I have a theory that there are giant worms that live deep in the magma of the earth, and smaller yet still massive worms that live above them - further from the core. You don't need evidence, it just makes sense, trust me. We can send satellites deep into the universe, but we can barely scratch the surface of our planet. That's because once you break out of gravity momentum does the rest of the work. The probe literally just sits still unless measured by the changing relative distance to other planetary bodies. But by that measure, I'm almost moving at lightspeed too.

Yeah, space is for pussies. If you really want to make a scientific discovery go down into the mantle of the earth. Nobody has yet. Our furthest drilling techniques don't even get 10 miles down I don't think. So it's best to stay poetically theoretical I think. If the world was a brain, and the trees were like the neurons of the brain - which they are, then every time a tree gets hit by lightning it's like a brain having a thought or idea. That's how our brains pretty much work, and the incidents of trees getting stuck by lightning is about the same as the
55

theoretical capacity at which our brains operate - 3-5%.

Trees are little fuzz on the surface of an organic being. The trees have a functioning economy and democratic empire just like us... or should I say one that we have innately modeled our social structure after. I heard somewhere that the ant population of the world outweighs the human population 9 to 1. At least it did in the 90's when I heard that fact and assumed it was true. The giant worms communicate with the ants via dirt birds that travel just faster than the speed of light. I have no other way to worship the great tree than to write a fashionable Haiku.

Must quench my fish thirst
Beluga in my pantry
A delicious treat

I guess one of my more relaxing hobbies is exposing systemic hypocrisy. I would probably be doing the same thing when Galileo was killed for saying the earth revolved around the sun. If I was around for the Salem witch trials, I would have pointed out the obvious flaws in logic that were killing countless innocents. It would almost give me pleasure to get burned into a bloody pulp for doing so. And if I was alive for Martin Luther posting those 95 theses, you could bet your sweet ass I would've been taking the "devil's advocate" side of his arguments. 1940's Germany though, I probably would have more or less rolled with the crowd... ya know, for the babes.

In all these situations there were people like me sort of flapping their wings into the wind knowing that it's pointless to try to shift the natural momentum. And that's how I see it. I think the number one problem in the world now is ignorance that allows people to be killed and imprisoned and kept in poverty, and willfully misled. It's a systemic pattern that keeps the poor poor. It stifles creativity with worthless efficiency - all dictated by a false narrative, and faulty logic.

People allow logic to get so fucked up in their heads to the point where they get tricked into simultaneously gripping to intense polar opposite beliefs about things like science, religion, or politics.

People suffocate in self-delusion when they build their perceptions of themselves and the world around them on these fundamental beliefs that oppose each other so strongly. Shit gets weird, people go crazy. Not crazy like I went crazy - unpredictable and out of place. No, I'm talking about crazy by the millions. I'm talking group-think. Predictable, in step with the rest of the collective that can't process the direction that this human condition is taking them.

There have always been social constructs that kept the poor and hungry from taking back their share from those that gathered all the wealth. And even though it now seems impossible with the wealthy so physically hidden out of sight, they only hold on to their wealth on paper and on computer screens.

I don't make much of a choice in any of these matters. Almost everything I do every minute of every day is driven by instinct. Even when I know there's no good outcome from my moves - like walking north for three days or blabbing on and on about world affairs with people that are only going to hate me for it, it's all just what I feel I want to do, what I would like to do, what the right thing to do is after internally weighing all the abstract constructs in my mind.

So yes, I have thoughts, and I write them down. I think they're pretty good sometimes. Everyone who steps out and says something of merit is shunned for it by the majority. You shun, I shun, we all shun. But I guess just like the sparrow doesn't exactly know why it spits out the tune it does, I don't exactly know why I gotta rap on these socio-religious hypocrisies all the time. That's just what's what man.

It could easily be said that the emotion behind my views on this human condition is pointless. But I would say that so is the emotional attachment to a song or a movie or a child. The heart chooses what it chooses to be passionate about. In the end, none of this really matters anyway. I don't see my voice and opinions and words as anything that'll change the world. I could care less about the place anyway. Let the house burn to the ground for all I care. I'm just passing through this world on my way to the ether or the great tree or whatever. I'm not just content to lose to win here, I invite the privilege to taste the sweet gravy of Copernicus and all those "Sophos logos" individuals that got to watch a world of children play in this sandbox world with their fancy toys and status symbols.

They say if you can't beat em, join em. That is what they say, right? And that is the prevailing logic. When you get right down to it, that is essentially why people work all week to pay their taxes and their mortgage. I say if you can't beat em, let them beat you. But they can't. And you know they can't, and that's fun. That is called slurping the gravy of Copernicus. Gosh, how did I get on to a rant about the state of the world? Do I have a problem? Am I mental? Seriously, am I?

As per standard, I get relief from my thoughts by going to the bar to take in some live music. I see a girl there, and in a drunken state of lethargy, I ask her if the polka dots on her shirt are real, to which she responds that her date is being lame let's go back to her place.

It's a funny series events getting to this girl's house, but when the taxi pulls us up to her place it's one of those ten million dollar mega mansions. When you live in Vail you either reside in a three-bedroom apartment with five messy roommates, or in a ten million dollar mega-mansion. There's really no in-between.

When we get there we have a dance party, just the two of us. A real sexy wild cat she is. She's 30 I think, has a real estate business or something like that, but I'm sure the money and house and all that stuff are her dad's. I think that's basically what she said. I don't know. She keeps playing music, then taking off her clothes and dancing really close and sexy. I like that sort of thing. It's nice. It's a nice feeling, and it's fun, like good sex.

About an hour into our little tryst, out of nowhere she lets loose with this outspoken Republican rant. She did warn me that she was crazy though... real crazy, like I wasn't going to be able to handle it. A curious specimen you are Ms. Tori. She's the real aggressive type that throws her politics all out there with all sorts of hateful righteousness and emotion. I let it slide though obviously. I'm not going to take the bait and get into an argument about the news of the hour with her. I make the kind of passive aggressive joke that you can only lob over a person's head once or twice before they stab you with a knife.

She has big boobs and a pronounced camel toe, my favorite. To have good camel toe, one must possess the attribute of "box gap" - otherwise known as thigh gap. It's very fashionable right now. All the great lingerie models have very pronounced box gap nowadays. Back in the 60s, all the fashionistas and movie stars had thunder thighs and wild bush, so there was no chance of seeing the light trace of tight clothing over the labia majora. Ooooo yeah, this dame gives me a real boner. We pop a bottle of champagne at around 3 am, and I guess I black out after that. I'm not nude when I wake up, so I don't think we got too crazy. I have to bolt out of there to get to work on time. In hindsight, I probably should have called out sick and enjoyed the morning, maybe made a little love. Oh well, next time.

I guess I've really been on a tear with the female persuasion lately. It doesn't really feel like it though because I don't think I've really found anything that I would consider love - nothing even approaching it. And again, I don't know why. There must be something wrong with me. There must be. Yeah, there was Jess that I met and smooched a bit with right before I left the country, then the kiwi and the jew princess in Thailand. Then last week when I drove to Aspen I met a gal at lunch one day and invited her to come with me camping, and an hour later we were off. We smooched a bit, then slept real close together in my tent. But that was mostly because it still dips below freezing at night and she was unprepared. She didn't bring anything really, just hopped in my truck and away we went. She grew up just ten miles from Brixton. She used to work in one of the mental institutions I was in. I don't tell her that, but do inquire what it was like to be around crazy

59

people all day. Another smart gal. Master's degree just like the rich dancing chick. Not that it necessarily matters, but it paints a picture; it tells you something. That's all those degrees really do. To be smart and acquire knowledge you look stuff up and practice things. Getting degrees has very little to do with the process of gaining knowledge in my opinion.

This thing with Rich feeling the need to defend the family from me just sets me off. When I try to figure out what kind of ideas he has in his head to make him think that, and where the heck those ideas come from, and why no one is talking sense into him about it... well it just makes me feel ostracized and vilified again. I thought that was a thing of the past, and I was so happy to be able to let that go. But it seems like it's still a very real issue, maybe even more drastic than it used to be. The son carrying on his father's legacy. It's a shame. I don't think a person should have to deal with this kind of business.

So, my mind is blown out a little. As every action has an equal and opposite reaction, I send a mind-blow back that way. I flush a universe turd down the grave. By that I mean I send a text to Rich, Vin, Joe and mom with a screenshot of a note I sent Ivan two days before the Knight Commander died. The note basically said that I intended to go back to Brixton, mend fences, leave the past behind, and make nice with Don despite everything. I was tripping hard on mushrooms at the time I sent the note - well, like I said... the universe and all that.

Christ, if I would have gone back to Brixton right before his sudden unexpected fatal reaction to a prescription drug he was taking they would have thrown me in jail for suspected murder. Even now Rich probably thinks that this text is proof that I killed his dad. But the simple truth is that the universe just wound out that way. I can't explain it. There's no need to. Shit happens.

I didn't send the family that message out of spite. I barely sent it at all. It was more or less just some sort of primal telepathic kind of transmission - like as a conduit of the universe does. I mean essentially

60

we are all conduits, right? Does that make any sense, or do I sound like a tube of toothpaste? It doesn't matter. Not that I'm anything special, it's just that when it doesn't matter anyway, when the ship is sinking, who cares when you jettison the silver planks. Hmmm, to the Brixton folks that look only for reasons to push the panic button, a message like that would probably have been terrifying. Well... oh well. You would think that after enough times pushing the false alarm button that people would chill out and relax. But it's quite the opposite. Their chronic paranoia only makes that urge seem more righteous. Go ahead, push it. Push it straight to hell mother fuckers.

Brixton rain, I don't remember too much of it. I remember running in it, playing basketball in it sometimes too I guess. I remember working in it building castles and highways. It rained on the late king's coronation as I recall, and again on the eve of the all souls moon, the black sabbath, and of course, on Tuesday.

Wars were fought in the olden days by two tribes of men. Some, like myself, believed that it always rains on Tuesday. That was what they were taught, and that is what they remember observing. Others, perhaps out of spite or madness, spread a rule of law mandating that Tuesday is the soul's day and that the soul is dry. Some factions believed the soul was dry and cold, other believed it was dry and hot like a log. But for the sake of war, those two factions put aside their differences to fight the wet Tuesdays. All men die - some in battle, some in hearth. We'll never know who was right, and I suppose that's why it doesn't always rain on Tuesday anymore... only sometimes as often as others.

As expected, my love hangover has settled in. I sent Tori a love text and haven't heard back from her in three days. If she's as crazy as she says she is, she's already had several fits of rage against herself for letting loose like she did with me that night. I tried to think of ways to deal with our political gap earlier today - because she's clearly even more close minded about Democrats as I am about Republicans. I'm not saying I'm a Democrat, but I'm sure that's the box she has put me in to make me her enemy. My biggest problem with people that call themselves Republicans is that to accept all their doctrines they have to be so close minded. I mean lacking empathy is one thing, but to close your mind to reality and proven mathematical scientific fact just for spite and to fit in with your neighbors, well that's just bizarre to me. I don't know that I could ever understand a person like that.

Ok, I mean if they were a rino for family reasons, I get it. I think maybe this Tori is a rino. I think a lot of them are rino's just to keep ties and have their elder Republicans feel proud of them - proud of themselves for creating mindless clones. A rino is an acronym for Republican In Name Only. I think Sarah Palin or Rush Limbaugh invented the term in an effort to shame people that start hearing an iota of reason from the other side.

I'm like Spock I think. I just can't understand the raw blind ignorance of these types. But that makes me just as bad, doesn't it? I can't empathize with that mindset, and therefore I fear it and dislike it. Does it make me a hypocrite because this entire group of people turns me off so much? You can tell when you read 19th-century Russian novels that this polarity and division have always been an issue in societies. But I think there's also always been an abundance of indifference through the ages when the prospect of hot sex is involved. And the devil laughs and laughs.

So even though I see absolutely no possible future with this rich gal, and knowing that any further encounter will probably result in more stress, I still felt a little deflated having lost the thrill of the prospect. What I should have done is never even contacted her back. That would have been the play I think. Now she gets to be the one to never establish contact. Maybe she's screwing a cash cow. Maybe doing cocaine and starving herself to keep that porn star body of hers. A gal in her situation has to be her very best or else not exist. That's probably why she knows she's crazy.

So whatever, it's just a silly deflation I'm feeling right at this particular moment. I don't know if I'll ever get anywhere in any kind of substantial love life. It's getting borderline ridiculous. I should have someone by now. I've been watering a nice plant (metaphorically - the plant being me I guess) and nothing has happened yet. Good earth, clean water, plenty of sunshine, ample growth... wait, this analogy stinks - plants don't fall in love or pair off. They just grow, shit seeds into the wind, then maybe they fall over and decompose. I am a great tree. I have been praising the great tree for so long that I have become one. Maybe if I praise this Jesus character everyone has been raving about I'll find peace, love, and happiness. That's basically what it says on the brochure. The love of Jesus is quite fashionable these days, while the pagan worship of a tree is considered outdated and crass. And therein lies my problem I suppose.

It's nice to hear Joey tell me that he has my back. I'm sure he wasn't supposed to tell me about the family's plot against me. He knows the landscape though. He knows who let me down in the past, and how hard it must have been for me to sit in solitary confinement for 3 hours waiting for that $60 bail to come through from any of the dozen friends I was sure would stand up for me. Then that next 3 hours, then the next 3 days, then the entire week after that, minute by minute.

A few weeks into solitary confinement with $60 bail and I was still counting the seconds. So there were another 4 hours of waiting around in a small box, then about another 45 minutes of thinking that maybe there is some way out of this hell hole since no one else has the balls to help me out, then another hour, then that night, then the entire next week. Everyone has had frustrating weeks, but could you imagine sandwiching them in between weeks spent in a small concrete box with $60 bail that anyone could get you out with, then add another few hellish days on either end before dealing with any of the actual tangible obstacles in your world?

Five weeks was an arbitrary amount of time that they made me wait for my trial. If they would have scheduled me in with the judge the next day, he could have just as easily found me guilty of trespassing or disorderly on that bus and let me go with 24 hours of time served instead of five weeks. Would anyone have posted sixty bucks for me if I was made to wait five months or five years? According to stats and case studies that I've read on the subject, probably not. It's a rabbit hole that I was lucky to escape from. It is a desperate situation for me and anyone else. With a simple lifeline from any loyal soul that would help an old friend so close, but impossibly far, a person goes mad. When a person screams for his innocence and demands release it's easy to overlook what came first, the accused crime or the imprisonment. It's easy to write it off as a situation the person got themselves in. But the mentality of folks that wouldn't help me, that let me stay locked up for 5 weeks could easily have left me to rot in there for 5 days, 5 months, 5 years, or fifty years. It's all the same, and that is a little scary to know when considering the idea of coming "home" to Brixton for a visit. If I were blindsided by this Rich thing, it would be a real possibility that I don't make it back to my real home in Vail. There's something wrong with that, and nobody wants to acknowledge it or own responsibility in any way. Not a single person. It's on me. In the end, any negative outcome would be my fault. Inaction on anyone else's part will be looked right past by the herd. This is part of the human condition. It's the Salem witch trials, it's the death sentence of Galileo, it's the rise of the Nazis, and the fall of reason in today's world. Everyone can say is not their fault. Everyone can avoid blame by avoiding the reality of the situation.

The light at the end of the tunnel though is the prospect of getting out. I knew it had to be only a matter of time. But there's no way to prepare yourself to be numb enough to go back in and out of fucking strait jackets and injection comas till you are beat up enough to admit that it was all your fault and that everyone was so justified in sending you to this place of healing.

Then, with any luck, you disappear and cease to exist.

Why the hell would I trust any fucking one of those sons of bitches to treat me like a human being if I ever came back to that strip mall, traffic light, corporate wasteland, church hive? Fuck that. Oh, so that Rich can win the heart of the ignorant masses by attacking me. He'd be totally justified since I'm the insane one. Christ. He literally talks about killing me and doesn't go to jail or something. I'd step foot in that town and be sent to the fucking nut house immediately if not sooner. That's just the fucking way it is. Fuck it.

Hey everybody. Have a great day. I did. Slept in, went to my coffee shop, played some golf, didn't read mail about debts I have, didn't feel the eyes of my neighbors looking at me walking to my car to go to work. Paranoid mother fuckers. Eat it, choke on it. I'm passively watching you from far far away. That incestuous slime hole.

Oh well. I should be able to wash my ole head out with some sports. I'd like to see Tiger win another championship or two... same with LeBron. I'd like to see Bernie Sanders win also. And Africa. My heart pines for mother Africa obviously. I'd like to see the feminists do a better job with the world they inherited, and I would like California to get the rain they need. And I would be happy to hear the voices of all the children in the world and all the angels in heaven unite in a glorious hymn of praise of the lord of hosts and the great tree of wisdom

Ancient Chinese Secret

Tragedy struck at Maroon Bells yesterday. A dad and his kid... or should I say, a kid and his dad hiked up the mountain range, were struck by lightning and perished their deaths. What a way to go. The universe gives you life, then sort of gives another life though your balls into another human woman's womb (for legal reasons it's not really life at that point, but whatever) then instead of committing babycide the zygote produces its own life; then grows, chews bubblegum for the first time, then a few more times, then one final time, then eventually toward the end of his life lays down in a tent with his father and dies via a massive injection of negatively charged electrons.

Pulmonary spectrometer indicates variations of density. Imminence pending. Recommended happenstance; fortitude.

There is a new thing with semicolons, have you heard? It's as fashionable as the ice bucket challenge. People are getting semicolon tattoos now for suicide awareness. The significance is that a semicolon represents a point where the author could have ended the sentence but decided to keep going. ... As I think about it though, the sentence will eventually have to end, or else it would be madness. Fun fact, the longest sentence in literary history is attributed to Proust, and I think he killed himself. So that should tell you something. God gave me tattoos of periods all over my body. Freckles. It's when the author... freckles.

All I do is work now. It's sort of like the old days when I was a fully functional member of society - before I became a fully fictional member of society. I guess I never took too much pride in the jobs I've held, at least not to the point of really feeling proud to tell anyone what species of corporate bull frog I was. I was always kind of happy with myself for holding these positions, but never overly proud to tell a chick about it. Being a bartender was different. Chicks dig a bartender, probably because he's basically on stage, and in the restricted area of the room. Eventually, I came to the realization that the kind of chicks that are attracted to bartenders are rarely worth their weight in fiber. It's like a dude being attracted to a stripper.

So now I'm a banquet man. I'm a cross between laborer, waiter, busboy, and bartender for events like weddings and corporate gatherings. I guess I could go ahead and try to move up and be a banquet captain. That would be like moving up in the army from private to sergeant. It would be the military equivalent of an e3 to e5 basically. Most dynamics of the working world operate much like the military with hierarchies and chains of command etc. E1 means enlisted 1st rank. O1 is the officer first rank, which was the pay grade I was at while in officer school.

In the corporate and professional world, just like in the military, the "E" versus "O" classification mostly has to do with whether or not you graduated from college. Each branch of the military names their ranks differently. For example, O7 is a rear admiral in the navy, but a brigadier general in the army. Napoleon came up with this whole system. That's why all the ranks sound French in dialect. The upper echelons like admiral or general would be the civilian equivalent of "C-Level" executives. CEO, CFO, CIO etc. Then there are board members that the C-level folks report to. They would be the equivalent of congressmen and senators I guess.

There are basically 4 ways to become an officer in the military. 1: ROTC - where you train during college in exchange for free education, 2: OCS - which is what I did, an intense 14-week indoctrination period, 3: graduation from the Naval Academy, and 4: a move from enlisted to officer. 4 is surprisingly rare though. It would be like going from nurse to doctor. Doesn't really happen. And it's nearly impossible to change branches - Marines to Air Force for example. It's weird because it's so random how you join. It's basically whichever recruiting center you walk into first.

The middle ranks are the worst. That's where all the ass kissing and back stabbing takes place. The reason your boss fakes a laugh at his bosses terrible joke is to continue to climb that ladder and chase that cheese. It's at this level where people are most likely to fool themselves of the human value of themselves or their peers. A vice president at the shoe factory seems so important to those below them in their hierarchy, but there are probably a dozen or so vice presidents living around your neighborhood, and as you know most of them are idiots with fake laughs and odd grooming habits.

Presidents are presidents in civilian and military; basically royalty like kings and queens - figureheads mostly. Small business owners are sort of like tribal leaders and don't have to adhere to such strict hierarchies. The role of the professional athlete hasn't changed one bit in all of human history. Gladiators outrank emperors in the eyes of society and always will, and will always have a harem of concubines to prove it. Jesters of the court are always wild cards and can be played as anything by anyone whenever they want if they are in the deck. Trump is trump and must be played if led. Donald Trump is a left bower until he ascends to Emperor.

It's crazy, if I had made it through two more months of officer school, not only would I have outranked an enlisted soldier with 25 years of experience, I also would have been giving that soldier orders on who to kill in retaliation for the 9/11 attack. As it happened though, I traded a walk-on part in the war for a lead role in a cage.

There is quite possibly an ancient Chinese secret to be revealed to me today. I'm floating; that is to say, I'm going on a float; on a boat, on a river - the Colorado River. The mighty Colorado. At this point in the summer though it's not so mighty. But in spring when the snow is melting it rages and swallows the life of many rafting humans.

The rafting season is half over, and this is only my first time out all year. I've made a promise to myself not to talk about this family mess with anyone. It's too fucked up, and will only spoil a good time. So it'll just be me, Libby, and Gus. Libby and Gus, Gus and Libby. What a couple of cards they are.

Libby's a trip. She's wearing her standard attire - sun dress, army boots, and two pairs of sunglasses. She owns this plane of existence once the acid kicks in. Gus is a tricky one to figure out and work into my patchwork of orbital socio-mechanisms. He's the popular kid. He's in with the in-crowd. He should be though. He's got a sharp wit, an infectious laugh, and skis like a champ. He has this cockiness and vulnerability going at the same time. But he's like a professional hippie. You can equal part love the guy and hate the guy. And he can, in turn, equal parts appreciate what you bring to the collective, and be threatened by it.

The whitewater of the day turns into a star shower by the night time campfire. Meteor zipping across the galactic disc for eons. So natural. So bright. Like nothing I could have ever dreamt of experiencing. There's lightning in the distance. What planet are we on, how did we get here? Oh, I remember, Red and White trail... Piney Mountain... I could get you there in a flash. It's right behind my house. Drive 600 yards, get on the dirt road, and go 10 miles straight to the top planet Earth.

My noodle oozes loony tunes. Good news, my snooze loses. Bad news, El Niño. Food news, the juice spoon loops. Toon frooze, Dew's Tuesday cruise. Good news, Tim made all-star this week. He goes to fruit school in the June. Bad news, his fast kin went. Good news, loose Lucy screws Lou Dong Fu! Why ride a dunkee into town when you can simply walk in on your damn 2woz.

Plain Moon Girl

I'm going on a date like a real adult tomorrow. It'll be just like in the movies and magazines. We'll meet at a fancy hotel bar at 8 pm on a Friday with nice shirts and polite conversation. It's with a girl that I met on Tinder - the fashionable internet dating site. It's the swipe game. Most people play while they poop I think. The whole time each of us will be asking ourselves and maybe each other intimate questions. Poking around for clues of warning signals, excuses to ditch this whole ridiculous event and run for the hills. I get the feeling I'll probably take her to pound town. Sometimes you can tell by the font of a person's jibber jabber. She's 34, brunette, petite maybe. That would be great.

It's not fashionable anymore to be chaste. You do what you do though, everyone always does... I mean either you screw or you don't. And skinny is the new fat now too. When did that happen? Probably in the cocaine and disco years. Skinny gals used to be hags compared to ole Beatrice the rotund back in the days of old. There was romance long ago, but the porn generation doesn't care about that. It's sad. It's sad for me to feel the conflict of being turned off by a girl that I know has banged this person or that, or has a tattoo or a dangling labia. It's not funny man, it dangles there in the breeze and I'm supposed to look at it, and feel fancy-free.

Tragedy strikes again, this time in the kitchen of dreams. Arthur is dead. We had a remembrance for him at the top of the mountain. He was an ornery old black cook from Mississippi or something like that... Alabama maybe. He was about 60 I guess. He's dead now but wasn't last week. Kitchen wizard. Everyone thought it was his Parkinson's because he had a tendency to shake a lot - his hands, arms, and lips would quiver steadily for hours. Turns out it wasn't Parkinson's at all, just extreme alcoholism. So that's a relief I guess.

The girl I was supposed to meet later in the day also suffered a tragedy so we decide to delay our first encounter. Her cat has endured the death. She killed it because it was old. She drowned it right in the bath tub. Just kidding, I don't know how she killed it, probably at the vet office like a normal person.

Since then we've swapped the dumbest 3 texts in the history of dating. She said something like "nice moon tonight" and a night later I texted back something like "tonight too". Then tonight she texted something like "and also tonight".

So this moon girl wants to try and meet up again. She looks so plain in her picture, it's awesome. God damn, I probably sound like a fucking girl scout writing in a diary right now.

And now I'm in love with the moon girl... the plain moon girl

The anticipation is killing me when we finally meet for our classic first date in a casual hotel lobby sushi parlor. Hello, how's it going?, good and you?, hmmm let's sit over here., sure, I'll have a water... 2 waters, and a menu, thank you. We look at the menu, pick out 3 rolls to order along with a beer for me and a glass of wine for her. We're both doing a fine job pretending this isn't too weird - complete strangers deciding if they want to begin a campaign of having sexual intercourse on a routine basis.

She asks how my day is going so I tell her about the pen that exploded in my laundry earlier and the efforts I went through in order to clean the mess up. There was someone else's towel in there with my clothes, so I think maybe that's how the pen got in there. It doesn't really matter; it would have been an accident anyway. That was a good opening anecdote I think; a story of trials and tragedy overcome with a good attitude. I didn't really plan it... but I think in the first date playbook they say you should have an anecdote ready, current if possible.

About 10 minutes into this fiasco I find myself talking about Slobodan Milosevic, the genocidal war criminal from the 90's. What the hell is wrong with me? It sort of fit into conversation, but that's a huge name to drop when first meeting a potential soulmate.

We were doing that whole thing where you say where you're from, and then maybe give a brief synopsis of maybe school or work or family until you find a common connection or interest. So I guess we referenced her dead cat maybe, leading to questions of past pets, which led to discussion of the places she lived, and we quickly discovered that she has lived in Vail all her life but then she goes to Austria in the falls to see her mama. Then she said how she drives around Europe while she's over there and mentioned Croatia. I said that that I heard it was amazingly beautiful countryside, but that it is most associated with the conflict in the 90's. She said yes... then I said Slobodan, then she said yes the war criminal accused of genocide.

We finish our splendid meal and I ask the waitress for our tab. I've already estimated what the bill will be, and have readied the cash so that I can pay like a gentleman and we can move on. But as I glance at the check I see that I don't have nearly enough cash in hand. I clumsily start pulling more cash out, and some of it falls out of my wallet onto the ground. Also flying out of my wallet are a couple pills that look like aspirin, but are in fact bipolar pills that I still take morning and night, and also keep in a slot in my wallet just in case I need to shut my brain up mid-day. So shit is flying everywhere, and I'm struggling to figure out how much to tip because even though the bill was higher than I expected there was a discount on it, so I'm supposed to tip on the pre-discount price. With all the money and pills zipping everywhere I lose track of how much is owed and how much I've already pulled out, so I just keep dumping bills on the table. First 20s, then a few 5s and a 10 spot or two, then another 20. I look at my pile of currency and throw all the 1s I have on top. The waitress and plain moon girl are watching me tap-dance through all my pockets pulling out more and more cash, pills, chapstick, pen, paper, and lint. It would have been nice to be able to cap the sequence off by pulling out a rubber chicken, or a link of scarves like the magicians pull from their pockets, but alas, it wasn't to be. In the end, I probably paid a thousand dollars for that meal, but it was totally worth it. She's great company.

We decide to have a couple more drinks outside at the Mexican restaurant next door and enjoy the early evening sunshine and fresh air. We're admiring the sky, mountain, and the athletic prowess of the kid across the highway on his swing-set. He's really going for it - way up over the cross beam on each swing. We watch in anticipation of his impressive dismount for a couple minutes but it never comes, he just keeps pumping away. By this point, we're talking like ole chums about this and that, no big deal. After our outside drinks, we walk to the Ale House at her suggestion. It's open mike night, there are all sorts of sports on the TVs, and they have a pool table. We both dig that atmosphere. She knows a couple people that happen to be in tonight, as do I. Vail's a small town.

The topic of Europe comes up again, and I mention that I'm thinking about going to Italy this fall once my work season ends. We discuss further and realize that our travel dates would overlap. We laugh that maybe we'll meet up or whatever. Like no big deal, maybe we'll meet up in northern Italy and explore the countryside and ancient ruins where I just happen to know the language and am as familiar with the capital as I am with Vail or Brixton even. Like hey, if you're in the neighborhood, we should hang out. Ya know, why not. So that's something nice to look forward to.

Too bad I'm not divorced yet. I think if a girl is dating a guy my age, they prefer that he's been married for 5 or 10 years. If they see someone in my position in life that's social and charming but never married, they don't look at that person like a good catch necessarily. They try to figure out what's wrong here. Is he some sort of freak? Is he making the time with a new girl every week? Some girls want it casual like that though nowadays. I'm so lost in this game of souls.

While we're playing pool, a girl comes up to me twirling and sort of throws herself at me for a minute to dance with her because it's her 25th birthday. So I oblige - standard swing dance twirl-a-girl moves for about 20 seconds. But so now my plain moon girl may assume that this happens all the time. She's sort of right... not all the time... like once or twice a month maybe. I can't feel guilty about that, right?

I walk her to her car with the intention of kissing her, otherwise, we'll be in this friend zone that will be tricky to move forward from. So we walk the hundred yards toward the sushi place, behind the McDonalds, and over this little rock garden that really isn't meant to be walked on. I'm kind of following her over the rocks and shrubs, which I had a few moments earlier decided would be the right spot to kiss her, and I said something like... I guess I'm going to give you a kiss now and then go back inside.

She turns right around, faces me, and there my face was, about 6 inches above hers at a range of around 15 inches and closing fast. Glance, contact, eyes open, eyes closed, a little tongue, a lip sucking maneuver, all in tune with a light coordinated sway side to side. About ten to 15 seconds and I pull away. Ok, see you later, it was fun. She gets in her car, starts it up and the lights are on me like a spotlight. I just walk away not looking back as I cut back across the rocks. The intention was to appear like I was basically walking off into the sunset. Later that night I text her that it was a nice moon tonight.

So now I have officially kissed my plain moon girl we are basically engaged to be married in a few weeks in the European countryside. Well, that's an exaggeration. But there's a good chance we'll hang out in Italy because it looks like we will both be in the region at the same time. I wonder what's going to happen with this one. It seems like we're both on the same page - fun, lighthearted, adventurous, learned. Sexy. It's troubling how often things with such promise end up falling apart. I guess sometimes you find out that there's a problem, an incompatibility. Like something that may be considered rude to one person is just a matter of fact way of living to the other. The first fight is I think the truest indicator of personality dynamics. I think my tendency is to carry passive aggressive grudges. It's a terrible character flaw of mine.

Summer Daze, August Nights

The mystery of the passing boner. I think it was about 5 years ago that mine failed me for the first time and ended a flowering relationship. It's the most depressing thing a man ever has to deal with besides the death of a pet or loved one. It's happened to me more than once. I mean not just a failure to launch on the first shot, but a scrap of the whole mission. I can think of 3 times that an otherwise awesome situation crashed and burned in a ball of flames. It's a restless night's sleep next to a naked person that you almost had sex with - especially when you've experienced the awkward let down of never getting another opportunity to show that person all your excellent orgasm tricks. Oh no, not again, I really like this one. If only this silly appendage would cooperate, she'd be mine forever.

It can be scarring. It can make a guy not want to put himself in that situation ever again. It's different for girls. If they're a little nervous and their parts aren't participating right away, they can always just slap some lube on it... unless they are on their period, or just done their period, or just starting their period, or somewhere in between. Then all bets are off. Better luck next time hombre.

So I guess that most women past the stage of routine dry humping have experienced the unexpected and unfortunate phenomenon of the lost boner. Any way you slice it though, there are a lot of highs and lows associated with this game, and tons of places to run and hide from it. Lately, I've been thinking about the advice that married couples get - that you really have to work at your marriage. It's not just an end game after you say "I do". I've been thinking that you have to work at that very same thing basically when you're single. In either situation, it's very easy to throw in the towel and just quit altogether. Happens all the time, especially after kids.

I think everyone's motivation to have sex with new people has been dramatically diminished since the use of porn and vibrators has become so routine for so many people. Unfortunately, living in the porn generation has raised the bar of what it takes to turn people on and get them off. Guys basically have to compete with military grade vibrators that take a girl to the moon and back in 2 minutes, and girls have to compete with the thousands of tight bodied sex cats that their man has been jacking off to for the last decade. So basically I think folks these days are more likely to be a bit more disappointed/self-conscious than they would have been a generation ago.

I told my new girlfriend that I would like to look at a group of trees with her, and maybe snap a photo or two. I alluded to many different groups of trees that I know around here, but she seemed unimpressed with all my scatterbrained ideas. There were many words I would have liked to say but couldn't, and there were many words that I did say but would have preferred to say in a different tone and order. Anyway, sounds came out of my face in her direction, and after a while, we ended up kissing under a new moon; which is to say we kissed under no moon at all. My plain girlfriend likes the moon, and I could not give that to her.

Nice moon tonight though. A crescent. We kissed closer to her car than the first time. It was in the next parking lot over. We were next to her gas tank. The first time we were about 10 yards off her front bumper. She drives a Subaru... which means she's probably a lesbian anyway.

I have a neck fetish. I fetish the neck. Oh, blast I fetish the fish neck. My pluck of flecks meshed the fuck. For her sake, I poked the flake, and sought the net for the fish with the speck in the nape of its neck. But all my love was in vain and she died in the rain. And I died in the rain several years later with a broken heart neck.

It's a real nice day you got here God… if that's who you really are. Thanks for the state of mind right now anyway. I hope when things turn sour I can remember that this feeling exists even if it's just passing like that leaf floating downstream.

Most of the snow in the high country melted a couple weeks ago so the water is just trickling through these days. Like my life, the current was dangerously turbulent a few months ago. I'm glad I got out on the river a couple times this summer though... the literal river I mean, not some metaphorical love-hate flow of unpredictable sometimes terrifying moments. Well, that too though.

What I wouldn't give for one more day of this life. If from some future point in my life I could come back to this moment and relive this day and this night and the next week, oh what a gift that would be. I'm sure. As it stands it looks like I will only have this one shot at making the most of the day. No pressure, it's really just another day. Besides the ambiance of this very beautiful sliver of the world right now, there really isn't any reason to want to live this particular day over. The days and nights are so similar anyway. But I know I have to cherish them. This lifestyle could go away so easily if I take it for granted, and I could picture myself wanting to give everything I have to relive this dream for one more day.

The years were ticking away so quickly in my old life. 30-year loan, 10-year degree, 6-year project, 3-year commitment, 5-year plan. I'm remembering my last day of work in my fancy corner window office corporate job in downtown Philadelphia. I went out on my lunch break and got a journal for the HR lady I had grown close to because she told me she was soon leaving the company, and the country for another job soon. When I got back to the office, I was told I was being laid off. That was right when the economy took a dump at the end of the Bush years. Millions of people like me were getting their walking papers. She knew it was coming but wasn't allowed to tell me. So she left with a journal to write in, and I left with total freedom and severance package to take where ever I wanted to go. Rich town, poor town, young town, old town, busy town, slow town. Small mountain town.

Now I have a new form of rush hour traffic to beat. My favorite mode of transportation; and people do it all the time here, is standing on a skateboard and having your dog pull you along. Ever see people do that? It's a funny town man. A mountain town. That's how some people get to work on a normal day. Tugged by dogs, riding a skateboard, eating an apple.

I'm talking to ma on the telephone and we go on a tangent of theological discussion of the stock market. Well, I guess I went there, well, she went there, and then I pointed out this spot on the road map of the collective consciousness of mankind. She tells me she's taking a Bible study class about the book of revelations. It's been a while, but my recollection is that it's very interesting writing, dripping with symbolism.

I tell her that I remember reading it in college and remember the topic of numbers coming up, and sort of how the devil or someone warns of numbers making the world go crazy, or to hell, or to chaos, or something like that. Even way back then I thought... duh, we're talking about the stock market. I don't think some people realize how the stock market affects everyone's world. It's not like sports gambling. If stuff goes weird in the stock market, there will be no food on the shelves in the grocery store, and no gas at the gas station, and that will cause people to murder each other. If there is a dark force trying to destroy humanity, that would be a very easy situation to manipulate. The devil is in the details, as they say.

Before the market crash 5 years ago, a lot of folks had around $500K in their retirement accounts, plenty of which grows in the stock market. When 20% of that gets wiped out, the sun still comes up, life goes on, but the product of the last 10 years of their working life is now gone. It's just gone. That's not nothing. Why did you get up and go to work this week... and the week before, and the year before etc.? That labor was all for nothing now. So what are you going to do to eat, make more money? You can't. You lost your job like everyone else. Too many people lose their job and there is no reason for the markets to try to sell food, so people go hungry, then get angry, then etc., etc., French revolution.

But, the sun will still come up. People will still be crazy, but just in a more volatile way. Again, I don't really care. I'm way up in the mountains anyway. We will be pretty shielded from the mass panic in the cities and suburbs. So what's the point anyway? I don't know. Maybe I'm making all this up... which is fun to do. But the thing is that my opinions and predictions are very much based on fact. But the fact is that to an ostrich with its head in the sand the sun has set anyway even though there is a river of Copernicus' gravy running right off its back

Oh Great Tree, Maker of the air that I pine, wind my mind with divine twine, grind my rind fine, and find me a rhyme line. We will all die dry Great Tree; while you will dye sky

The children are not acting like themselves anymore. Summer is gone and they sense that this is schooling season. Their elder kin are going back to the school house grind for the second or third time even, and they can passively feel the dread. At least football season is upon us now. That's a consolation.

My soul sister Siena and I are enjoying a pleasant lunch under a shaded umbrella at one of the Italian side street cafes in the village. She runs the coffee shop where I go to day dream from time to time. She decided to let the dudes run the joint while we dine today. We share a bruschetta appetizer then she has the Greek salad and I the Italian sub with prosciutto.

She has a great smile, a very pleasant disposition, intelligent, young, blonde, loves yoga and the spiritual peace of mind that it brings her. Hmmm, why don't I date her... am I dating her right now? Doubtful. The topic creeps into conversation though. She's telling me her frustration with dating people is that here she is, a great catch, but guys don't ask her out for some reason. I tell her that yes, I often feel the same way but to a lesser degree. She's a pretty girl living in a town full of dudes. I'm not nearly as attractive to the opposite sex, and the odds are stacked against me, but still, it shouldn't be so impossible to find a partner.

One problem is that this is such a small town. Everyone knows everybody else's business. There's a saying here "you didn't lose your girlfriend, you lost your turn". It's true, and it sucks to know the gal you still love is banging your friends now. Just ask Gus - he hasn't been the same since he and Siena split up. Another problem is that this is a party town, and when people move here they often get wild for the first couple months. If they end up living here for a couple years they are going to run into all the dirt bags and creepers they regrettably slept with back in the day. Again, it makes it difficult getting close to someone when you know they've already been with a handful of your friends. It's just a part of life here.

The more universal problem in both big cities and small towns is that to make that leap from friend to lover you have to risk potentially making a good relation go sour out of awkwardness if your physical contact or display of affection is ill received. We agree that in younger years it was easier for things to come together because we didn't know about these things. When you were young and inexperienced you went out, kind of got drunk with someone, and kind of remember hooking up with them, then maybe see them at the bar again, and then all the sudden you're boyfriend - girlfriend. It's just not like that anymore. Siena is about 10 years younger than me and has previously told me that she really only likes to date older men that have their shit together to a certain extent. I tell her that often times I avoid good girls like her because I feel like I'm not really good enough. It's an honest dialog.

Of course, it sounds like maybe I should make this babe my babe, but I can't stick around for too much longer. I have to run to my next date with plain moon girl. "Buckets and Brews". It's an event that she invited me to with her friend the married couple. For ten American dollars, you get two American light beers and one American bucket of golf balls to strike into the distance of America in your chosen direction with your attained skill level at your leisure. She's left handed and just learning. I've never swung clubs left handed either, and wouldn't you know it, I'm a natural. I just basically pretend I'm swinging a tennis racket backhanded. It's almost more natural than the normal right handed golf stance. We have a nice afternoon and confirm plans for our next date - a road trip around the Italian countryside and southern Austria.

So yes, the rumors are true. I live in Vail and am officially dating a girl that seems very plain and nice. And I believe she is, but I can't figure out how that happened. She's lived in a party town since she was a tiny toddler of a woman. Then she went to college in Austria to get a plain degree, then moved back to Vail. My new plain girlfriend that I am going to Europe with that I have not yet felt up lives on my rocky mountain. It's very plain and beautiful just like my squeeze.

My squeeze
makes my knees
buckle

She and me
will see
a movie

She is plain
I feel fine

How about that for a poem. Some would say it's terrible, but I say it meets all qualifications. It portrays a feeling, rhymes, has a set pattern, and also rebelliously bypasses grammatical doctrines, which I think is pretty rad. I guess I just need to do the pattern a few times to nail it down. This girl must be a spy or something. How else can she be so good and awesome and plain all at the same time?

Cousin from Another Dozen

Ciao cugina Mila!

Come stai? How's the convent life kiddo? I think the last time I saw you was at Grandma and Grandpa's dinner table shortly after you became a nun. You and your sister were singing for Grandpa. I can't tell you how often I think of him and things he said... his smile... his Pegasus stories... and how much he like to work in the yard. He is one of the most influential people I have ever had the fortune to know in this world.

Guess what! I'm coming back to Rome! I've wanted to come back ever since my study abroad there. I can't believe it's been 15 years. I'm not sure if you've heard, but I live in Vail, Colorado now. It's so amazing here, so beautiful. I hope you can come visit someday. I'm still figuring out logistics and timing, but I plan to fly into Northern Italy in early October. A friend of mine from Vail will be in southern Austria visiting family at that time. We're planning to meet up and explore the lakes outside of Milan and then work our way to Rome. I understand that it probably wouldn't be proper for us to crash on the couch in the Vatican, but if you could recommend a place to stay in Rome, that would be great! I figure we'll probably be there for a week or two in early November.

By the way, I love, Love, LOVE the new pope! Love everything about him. I think Francis was my favorite saint in elementary school. Chose the life of a beggar over the life of a rich man, cool! Talked to animals, super cool!!! Don't tell anyone, but there's a rumor going around that he puts on commoner's clothing at night sometimes and walks around Rome on his own. I know he catches some flak for his progressive words, but I think what he is doing for the church is really amazing. His strong advocacy of systemic care for the poor seems very serious and genuine especially when he gets into specifics of fundamental changes that need to happen in our social and economic structure. I know he has to walk a fine line, but I and many people I'm close with get an honest feeling of open-mindedness toward people that have often been marginalized as sinners for things outside of their control and situations that they were born into. So if you see him in the hallway, tell him I said thanks for being awesome. I wish him lots of luck and a long life.

So, write me back if you get a chance. I'm really excited for this trip and am looking forward to catching up. A funny thing about cousins is that even if it's been like ten years, when you see each other you pick up exactly where you left off. And usually for me, on either side of the family, it involves laughing around a table till your drink comes out your nose.

Love ya,

J

. . .

Mila is one of the nieces of the Knight Commander of the Equestrian Order of the Holy Word. Her name used to be Rebekah until she became a nun. Her dad Jim is my dead step dad's brother. He's awesome. Probably my main influence in learning how to swing dance. He met his second wife swing dancing. She was gorgeous, had a Ph.D. in classical music or something like that I think. They adopted 2 girls but the marriage fell apart pretty quick. I remember Rebekah crying at the wedding. Really crying from her soul. Jim then remarried his first wife - Mila's mother. He makes the hilarious joke that the divorce just didn't work out. Ha! He's great.

His mom sent me a beautiful letter the other day, so I called her back to thank her and have a chat. She's always a fun one to talk to. She's so sweet and lovely. She's lived in Brixton ever since grandpa died a few years ago. It's crazy, I think she was still a teenager when they got married. I'm not sure if that was before or after he got back for WWII. She tells me she's lonely and bored. She longs for the life she had in New York. She has shrunk to a height of about four feet small. I can always tell that she's used to people talking to her like she's an elderly, but we usually break through that strange parlance after a few minutes. I think it's silly to talk to children, old people, or authority figures any different than you would to any other peers. It makes your words seem phony.

I tell her I'm calling from my street-side coffee shop and that the weather is nice. She says she'll be right over and laughs. So funny she is, like a child. She said she also used to hang out at places like this in her younger years... and smoke a cigarette. She said it like she was guilty of being bad. Like a child. She says she used to smoke three packs a day.

Like all grandmothers, she always goes out of her way to tell me how much she loves me. She tells me she has ever since I was just an infant. It's news to me that she's known me for that long since I don't really remember the Knight Commander being around until I was in kindergarten... but I guess I don't really remember anything being around before kindergarten.

Out of nowhere, she tells me that she had a really bad childhood with her family, but that she just had to let it go. She says she couldn't understand how someone couldn't love me and appreciate me as a blessing. She never mentions her son's name when she says this, but we both know.

I always thought she and Don had a strange interaction. He would talk to her in this bizarre baby voice; to mom also. Then at other times, he would take a whole different tone - aggressive and belittling. He sure was a strange cat.

I hear there's going to be a lunar eclipse tonight so I call up my pal Claire to see if she wants to watch it with me. We drive to a nearby mountain top and park in an open field around the top of the tree line and sit on the roof of my truck to watch the show. The full moon comes up over the east horizon just as the sun is setting on the west horizon. As it is still low in the sky, the left side of the moon starts to disappear from about 7:30 till 8:30. At 8:50 the whole thing is dark... and it's red. A blood moon. A blood moon on its own is amazing, but this was a blood moon eclipse. At around 9:15 the left side of the moon shines just a tiny bit of light. As the earth moves out of the way and that moon starts to reappear and I can picture the sun rising in China.

The eclipse takes about 45 minutes to pass. It's the most incredible celestial event I've ever seen. This whole time the sky is crystal clear. We see dozens of shooting stars, and the galactic disk is sprawled all the way overhead from the north horizon to the south.

The earth has moved out of the way, so the sunlight is once again bouncing off the moon in our direction lighting up the entire landscape. We can see a full panoramic horizon of the neighboring mountains 50 miles in every direction. The moonlight seems brighter than mid-day sunlight. I think the lack of color in moonlight sharpens the contrast of the surroundings and actually makes it easier to see. I make a fire. Claire hangs around for a bit before she goes home. I spend the night burning wood and laughing at or pondering whatever thoughts come and go. So many girls, not enough moons.

I have to go to Italy soon and meet my plain girlfriend in Verona... I think she'll be my girlfriend. But then again, I thought Claire might have kissed me back while we were sitting on the roof of my truck watching the blood moon super eclipse. That wasn't my goal in inviting her there. If it was I would have taken her to the car wash... but then I would have missed the eclipse. You would think though that after watching 20 years of romance comedy movies she would have fallen for me there. Strange gal. She says she needs to compartmentalize her sex from her emotions. She prefers to fuck people that she doesn't really like. I don't get it.

My fair plain lady love flies out to Austria tomorrow. I offered her a ride to the airport, but she said that she is going in the company of another man. And she didn't expressly say it, but she implied that she loves him more than me. He is older than me and he is also her father. I think he is a better skier too. Can she love us both? No, it's not possible. She can love only him and herself. It's ok though. I'll get by.

Christ on a cross. What a nice charm to have on your necklace. That crucifixion really was the most passive aggressive gesture of all time. I was such a goof when I was a kid. I used to actually try to live my life like Jesus. He was the freakin son of freakin God, man... or so the story goes. He didn't have to be up there. I mean he didn't put himself up there. And neither did I really when they strapped me down and put a needle of sedative in my veins and kept me doped up and confined to small communal living quarters with vagrants and drug fiends. Hey, all you lock-up artists, sorry you didn't flunk the Navy like me, but you didn't try either. Go throw a stone at Jesus you ignorant whores.

One nice thing about having a hometown that is a living breathing den of snakes is that by comparison the entire rest of the world feels very inviting and just happy to have you around. I talked to that mom of mine and she told me not to come to her house - for several reasons. I knew the one reason - Rich has some sort of death wish against me and a handful of guns in his possession. So if I visit either of the grandmas I need to call ahead first to make sure he's not there. So that one I understand. I ask what these other reasons are, and she says she's not comfortable with me in the house because I never wanted to go there while Don was still alive. So I'm basically banished from the house. She also says that there's a big presence of Don in the house, and she wouldn't want me to be there knowing how I felt about him. Like as if I would be a Muslim desecrating the holy shrine of the late great Templar of the Holy Pentecost wheelbarrow.

I felt the need to remind her that the reason I used to not go there was that the lead scientist in charge of paying the mortgage for her shrine to himself was kind of a dick to me for 25 years. But what good would that do? And there's no need to bring up the times that he got rough with me, that's just man stuff I think anyway. A rite of passage maybe.

Actually, no, fuck that... that's the poisoned mindset that perpetuates generations of abuse. Obviously. And, come on, you can't make a kid eat dinner in his underwear as punishment for forgetting to zip up his fly. Well, either way, for better or for worse, nothing of that sort really bother me anymore. And even though it's a quick flashback every time

I check my fly, I've never forgotten to zip it ever since.

It's small potatoes. And in all honesty, small potatoes are the best ones. Chop em up, fry em with lots of butter... delicious. He was always under a lot of stress. He would sometimes yell at me for not making an effort to talk during dinner. That was a hard task to work with as the most awkward socially inept child you've ever seen. I tried to tell a joke at dinner one time but I was like 7 or 8, and didn't know it was racist. He had just gotten out of a corporate sensitivity training and he passed along the knowledge that you can't refer to black people as black. You have to say the person with the gray shirt or whatever. I used to have to take out my retainer to eat and I was told to soak it during dinner time in a glass of water with these tablets that fizz and clean it, but he never liked where I put the glass, so I would get yelled at for that... and if my watch beeped at the top of the hour I'd get yelled at because he didn't like that. And if he yelled at me in front of holy infant Rich he would yell at me for making him yell at me in front of holy infant Rich. So there was a lot of that. I was always getting hit over the head with his insults and condemnations. That's why I didn't like the guy. Not because he spoiled his kids, not because he started dating my mom while she was still married to my dad, not because he was a big ole hypocrite. That stuff happens in life, and it's not really a big deal. I just didn't like him because he was very personally mean to me for a long long long time... the whole time. For him, it was half his life he spent being mean to me. For me, it was about 90% of my life. So I'm just hard-wired to hate the guy.

...oh, and the fact that he pitted ma against me. She always took his side in the quietest way possible. She would literally sit there, literally night after night while we literally had our talks that literally consisted of him talking about all the bad things I did during the day, and what my character flaws were. I literally had to keep a log book of all the things I did good and bad during the days so that we could discuss them at our nightly talks that were literally an hour-long talks. I literally still have the log book. It's a literary masterpiece that still resides at my dad's house.

I wish I had a time machine so that you could watch these nights from the window. It was really bad. She would literally sit there silent. He literally did 90% of the talking. I did about 7% of the talking when I would try to defend myself, and she would chime in for about 3% if he asked her for a second opinion on his assertions that my points are despicable and wrong to say or even think. I would walk up the stairs for my bed time feeling exhausted and just beat up and sad and sometimes angry. But I never yelled.

Rich yelled though. Holy shit, that kid would rage! Wow! I wish you could see that from the time machine too. He would curse them out so bad, and punch holes in the walls, and just go completely ape-shit. He'd run away from home and not go to school for days at a time, then be back in his room getting drunk and smoking pot, playing on the latest video game console they bought him for some holy occasion.

I think they all think of me as this loose cannon that might go off like a time bomb if I was around. That's why I think I wasn't invited to the funeral noodle. I think ma actually thinks I would destroy her shrine if was there - like that's what I've been plotting all along. It's too bad. I'm just curious what the place looks like now. I lived there 5 days a week for 15 years. The memories of that house are going to live there in all our minds whether I am present or not. Denying my physical eyes from seeing its present state only encapsulates the past. That house is like an old tree I used to climb decades ago. I'm curious how it looks now that both I and this metaphoric tree have aged so much. I think every person should be able to go back to the trees they used to climb... for the rest of eternity. That's just my humble opinion though... obviously.

I like taking walks down memory lane when I go back to Brixton. Sometimes I pop into my old high school and just walk down the halls and remember four years of memories. Peek in the classrooms, and remember four years of classes. But my feet can only walk down two kinds of roads, my eyes can only look through two kinds of windows, my nose can only smell two kinds of hallways. I can touch and twist and turn two kinds of doorknobs. I can visit the shrine of the Knight

Commander or The Great Tree in the heart of Rome. I suppose I'd find God at the shrine of the Knight Commander; or truth, wisdom, and love at The Great Tree. And though it's only my opinion, I may be right or wrong, I think I'd find them both in the Grand Canyon at sundown.

Bean Shop

If I've seen it once, I've seen it a dozen and a half times - this construct of human existence. The world is the way it is because of the fabric of human nature. And it doesn't follow logic in any way. It is chased by logic. But the world around us exists because someone is trying to gain someone else's love. That's a strong force and impossible to define, especially when you multiply it by 7 billion people with the same modus operandi.

What makes the grass grow? Blood blood blood! That's a line from the movie Full Metal Jacket. A metal jacket is the casing of a bullet FYI. Why does blood make the grass grow? Well, that's what they tell Marines in a sort of twisted funny sing-song kind of way in order to add another layer to the normalization of killing another human because you are told to. Who tells you to? The guy that follows orders best. How is it that we conceive of one man named Hitler killing 6 million Jews? Well, he was in love with Eva Braun. He was a painter. He had a knack for public speaking. What was really moving that machine? I don't know. I'm not obsessed with it. I am however obsessed with the hunt for why people do things, and why people don't do things.

There was a foot soldier in that army that only lived in his hometown with his kin. His motivation and the motivation of those around him created the world that those kids grew up in. Many of those kids ended up in the camps. Some of them play the flute, or practice dentistry now. They have dogs and are in love with people other than their wives. They build fences, and study trees and stars. They worry about the money they have, what they owe, and all of these things go into the equation of the next thing they do and say. Why do they talk about this or that? Why do they say what they say, with the inflection they use? How do they choose the people to talk to? What do they really think about when they look at the stars or other mysteries?

Sex and babies are not mysteries to the common man. No, they're functions to be measured and handled properly. They are serious things. Stars aren't serious things though. They are a mystery if one chooses to look at them as such. And many do, but rarely does it make them drop everything and wander into the ether. Where would that get you? Nowhere. The mystery is drained from sex and stars because the landscape has been defined. Penis size, money, social definition - these are pretty universal notions that come into the mind of man as he contemplates his urges and how to act on them.

History. I'm going to Rome to explore history and art and society. I am going to listen to the foreign tongue with my open mind. I've done this before. It's my mission, my ministry, my calling. It's the barrel I'm in, and it is headed toward a cascade over the Euphrates, into the Ganges, up the Nile, through the wormhole, and to the shore of the Tiber River where Romulus and Remus suckled their life blood. I speak of course, of Rome.

John Lennon once said that if he was alive in those ancient times and had the means, he'd live in Rome. He said he lived in New York City because that's the Rome of today. That was 1980 when he said that... or maybe the late 70's. He died 35 years ago. I booked my ticket to Rome a few hours ago. I leave from New York City. It's like as if John Lennon had a son in his imagination, named him Sean in real life, made him real after his death and brought his new world to my old one on the way to market.

Which market? What market? With which witch market? The Italian meat market, that's what. I think plain lady moon will meet me there. Maybe at the airport in her mom's car. Wouldn't that be nice? It's a relatively simple undertaking though, and quite fashionable.

Time ticks forward a few days and I unexpectedly acquire the sadness. It's an affliction. Does accepting it as such make me a pussy? Do I just have a bad attitude and negative outlook? I don't know, I don't think so. As best I can tell this is just as much of a disability as headaches, panic attacks, and seizures. In many cases, they prescribe the same medications for all these things. I'm considering faking a dizzy spell/headache the next time I have a crippling acute PTSD paranoid depression. That way I can sit in a dark corner and let it pass without trying to explain the underlying causes. Everyone understands physical pain. Headaches come and go with the wind just like these fragile mental states. So maybe I need to fake the ache. I try not to let this head full of dust slow me down. Well, that's not exactly it... I try not to try to not let it slow me down. It's a passive subtle game of inches in my mind. Meditation helps sometimes. Lots of quiet.

But there's a weight on me now, it's in the rain. And it weighs more on a heavy day. My mouth is dry and my shins are sore. My boot heels pine for warmth. My good girl is long gone a fly, and the mast of my ship is at the impound with a hundred note ticket. I have 4 daughters that each have kin by men of low rank. My heart beat is irregular. All these things and more would be the envy of my neighbor, and that makes me sad because I don't appreciate my own good fortune. I have a rusty cylinder in my car that compromises the entire apparatus. Last Christmas, at mass they spread my ashes. My asses are stuck in molasses, and the gas in pap's ass is atrocious.

The sadness though, it's ok. It doesn't hurt too much this time... right now. There's a numbness. Sorry. I'm lost I think. And I'm afraid I just attract hammers upon my head every time I speak or write, or look at anyone in their eyes, or do anything. Doing nothing is ok. A state of catharsis feels fine. A natural state of catharsis. Does that word mean what I think it does? I forget. Sounds right. I sit. I sat a few minutes ago. I sat still on the side of my bed for a minute, then when I felt it was safe I put my head in my hands. Then I was able to open my eyes and drain my spirit. No, not like that - I didn't cry. I was able to release all feeling and numb it all down. All the...

It's just a headache of sorts I guess. Gosh, I have an actual head ache now. I'll try putting on sunglasses...

There, that's a little better. I'm facing a new wall now too which is a nice change of pace. My stupid worthless diplomas hang on the wall in the back corner of my bedroom. I hate my life but only for short stints, and not for any tangible reason. It's natural I think. People deny it its place, but I think in order to achieve true honest happiness you need to hate your life from time to time.

It's hard for me to see my forest from my trees. I think maybe I'm hung up on fallen leaves. No that's not it. My hand is in front of my face. That's the problem. Just hovering in front of my face at a range of around an inch and a half and it prevents the light of the world from reaching my frozen eyeballs.

My mind is deteriorating. I can never remember what I did yesterday. It can be frustrating. I can sort of feel the impression that yesterday or last week gave me, but I can't really remember anything anymore. I have to write things down a lot for day-to-day / hour-to-hour tasks. Yes, I knew it would happen sooner or later, but I guess I have the early stages of... what's it called... where you don't remember? Amnesia? Alzheimer's? Hemorrhoids? One of those brain deteriorating things. I'm pretty good at faking though because I remember feelings about smells or days or people. But then lately I'm realizing that I can't trust those instincts either anymore. Microexpressions I see on people's faces may or may not be real. Like it's good if you can pick up on them when playing poker, but if you see them in a quick interaction, and take it as a clue to another person's feelings or past impressions, it can be a little unreliable when you realize that you might be having a micro hallucination. Just last night at work I had to accept the fact that I just don't know what's going on outside of the moment. Luckily I still have a good grasp on the moment most of the time. Faces look the same to me a lot. I talk to people, and I know I recognize them, and they recognize me just fine and know my name, and talk about the thing we did or were talking about last, but I have no idea. It's been like that for a while now. I've been chalking it up to knowing and interacting with too many people. I think I meet a new person every day and learn their life story. I never really mean to. I think I must just ask simple questions or accidentally make some sort of gesture that gets them to quickly spill the beans on their whole existence. These lives blend together though. So the next time I meet that person a week and a half later they remember me as one of five people on the planet that knows their life, but I just can't recall who they are. So I fake it with another open question, which only brings on more beans.

My styrofoam cup
is open for business
my business is that of the beans

My open bean shop
can't keep track of the listless
riding a river of dreams

3

The Fall of Rome

It's Nice

It's relatively easy to get to most towns on this planet - you find your destination on the list, buy the tickets, sit in your assigned seat, and in a matter of hours or days you're there. I start my voyage at a friend's house in Manhattan, hop a few subways over to JFK, fly across the Atlantic, connect at the Naples airport up to Millan, then get on a train to Verona. Plain moon girl drives down from her family's place in Innsbruck to meet me there.

She had given me the name of a little hotel in town that she booked a couple days earlier, but I run into a logistical challenge. The problem is old cities don't exactly name all their streets. Also, the place isn't set up on a grid like modern towns. Its winding roads are more laid out like a bowl of spaghetti, so finding one particular human at one particular time-space coordinate is a whole other game.

I can't find a cab driver at the Verona train station that speaks English, and I don't have a map of the place yet, so the best I can do is get dropped off in the vicinity of the district that Ms. Moon directed me to the last time we talked. That'll have to do until I can get to a wi-fi spot to send her a message. I'm wandering around with my big orange backpack when I hear her call to me from the side of the side street I'm passing. She had just arrived herself and is parking her car.

It's funny, this sort of feels like a first date again... when in fact it is already our fourth. After a warm hello I drop my pack in her car and we wander around this beautiful town all day, drinking wine, espresso, eating, laughing, exploring. It's a thing of beauty. We're just as captured as all the other casual lovers in this city of dreams partaking in all the little pleasures to be had.

After waking up the next day, but before getting out of bed, I roll over and curl up with her, kiss her neck, slowly feel her whole body, and we have the kind of morning people have been having in Verona for a thousand years or more. This girl really turns me on man. I mean I love the way she kisses, especially on the slide just out of sight in the public arena. Sexy body, I mean just exactly my type - short-ish, tight waist, but fit and healthy, athletic and with feminine curves, and soft skin. She has Hazel brown eyes and sort of frizzy hair. It's not really long or short… average length, plain, like the moon. Her body is set and natural to her habits and hobbies, and her skin is settling on her face and frame as a mature grown woman. To me, that's hotter than a 20 something lust doll.

We spend another day in Verona before continuing around the northern Italian countryside to a nice town by Lago Garda - a huge beautiful lake nestled at the base of the Alps just north of Milan. The plan was to play around in northern Italy before she goes back to her plain moon ranch in Austria, but since we're having such a groovy time she invites me to come back with her if I want. I want, so we go.

The lack of sleep catches up with me as we make our way north. Every time we get in the car I'm either in high spirits enjoying the company and scenery or completely overcome with a physical and mental shutdown that only allows me to open my eyelids if my eyes roll up into my skull. I could sort of be mentally awake, but unable to see, speak or move, so I surrender and let the ride warp away a hundred or so kilometers at a time before waking up again somewhat refreshed in a new moment.

After several of these flashes in and out of consciousness in the night-time winding ride up and down the Alpen passes, we come to her hometown. The time space warp is over. It dawns on me that this girl I've barely been dating for a couple weeks is pulling up to her house, and is about to introduce me to her mom, and grandma.

It's nice though, very casual and comfortable. They're a very inviting family. The house they live in is actually a sort of restaurant / B&B. It's late at night but they have food and drinks ready for our arrival. They're speaking German to each other, but they switch in and out of English to include me in the conversation. I wonder if they know better than I do what the heck is happening here.

Coffee and breakfast are ready for me when I get up in the morning. They want to show me around the area for the day, so the four of us take a ride to get some food and drinks in plain moon grandma's hometown that's only about 20 miles away. How crazy is this? I mean moment by moment, task by task, no big deal. But when they decide to stop at their family cemetery on the way home to do some grooming of their kin's graves, I think geez, this seems like the kind of things that families do together. It's nothing I've ever done before. What does this make me?

I stay with the plain moon women for two more nights but in my own bedroom. I keep thinking about slipping into my girl's room for a little play time, but I decide against it thinking it would be rude or disrespectful. On my last morning there as I'm packing up to leave I regret my decision. It was a total missed opportunity and would have been lots of fun for sure. Dummy. Oh well.

So that's that. I would say our fourth date was a success. It'd be nice to keep this thing going, but she already booked her flight back to the states. I think we'll be a steady thing back in Vail. It was fun falling in love in Verona. It's a rare thing to fall in love with a local plain moon girl in a foreign land, and have her to come back to at the end of an adventure. I like it. It's nice and quite fashionable.

I'm cutting it close getting from her place to the train station to the Munich airport for my departure to another foreign land. The gals insist that I have a good breakfast. Maybe they're trying to make me miss my flight. You never can tell what kinds of tricks women have up their sleeves when they're trying to fix their daughter up with a suitor.

Well, in any case, I make it out of there, luggage and sanity mostly intact. Next stop Sicily, or Sicilia as the natives call it. But what the hell do they know naming things? As we approach take-off, my eyelids are impossibly heavy, and my eyes are rolling up into my skull.

Around the Boot

As usual, after landing I make my way to the taxi/bus depot to see if someone can give me a ride to the lodging I randomly reserved a few hours ago because it was cheap and seemingly central to the area. I think my taxi driver is in the mafia. He drops me off at the hostel and I give him a handful of local monetary units. I'm pretty sure the front desk girl that shows me my room is also in the mafia, but I'm not sure if it's the same one.

After two days in Catania, I've come to believe that everyone is in the mafia. It turns out that my Italian sucks so I'm struggling to even order food at the cafe. The local map that found its way to my pocket has plenty of landmarks and points of interest, but I can't seem to find them even when I'm standing right on top of their coordinates. This town blows.

Someone at the hostel convinces me that Siracusa is the next place I should go. Who am I to argue? For some reason English speaking people call it Syracuse because apparently, we know how to name their home better than they do. In fact, we've even named a great basketball college accordingly, a fact that I and the guy next to me on the bus are discussing at great length. Who could forget that 7 overtime game leading into the NCAA tournament in the late Bush Jr. years? His girlfriend apparently. They live in a little timeless paradise on the Italian mainland just south of Rome. I think one or both of them are in the mafia, but I can't be certain. Ah, the international language of basketball. Paulo and I talk the rest of the ride about the intricacies of the Spurs team dynamics, and of course LeBron - a man amongst children in the NBA.

It becomes apparent to me when the three of us get off the bus that people don't actually speak Italian in Sicily. Tourist books say that the people speak "dialect", which I thought meant a different pronunciation of the same language. But even Paulo is unable to get directions to town from the bus station. Luckily, the owner of the mafia hostel I was staying at in Palermo gave me good directions on how to get to his cousin's place in the heart of Siracusa, so eventually, I make my way to my next dwelling. This place is nuts. I'm in some pimp condo behind the street market, next to the dock where Homer landed in 300 BC and really put this place on the map. I don't know, whatever. I'm exhausted and just want to take some simple creature comforts while I have the chance.

I awake with a head full of crud. I can't figure out why. It happens all the time, and it doesn't matter what world surrounds me. I need to do a better job living outside of myself. After a cup of coffee and stroll around the village, I still don't know what this feeling is. Usually, I can figure it out, trace it back to a bad thought. Well, in this case, I can't. Maybe it's just me coming off of the high of the last few weeks of transition to this point of solitude.

They call this town the white city, and it's easy to see why. Apparently back in the days of the plagues they used to cover the place in lye to disinfect the town. They've kept the tradition of that atheistic ever since.

I spend two days exploring every inch of this coastal wonder. It's such a tiny town that I've bumped into the same locals a couple times already while taking in the street music scene. On my last night in town, we rock out in this tiny little cafe till the sun comes up. I could have stayed, but I'm restless to move on. I want to get onto the mainland of Italy, but the logistics are frustrating. Sicily doesn't make it easy to get off the island. I keep seeing these cruise ships coming and going and I think to myself that there must be a way to hop on board one of them to the next stop along the Mediterranean. One of them has to be going my direction. Too much paperwork though. I can't even figure out which building to go into to speak in a language I don't know about this ridiculous idea I have.

So it looks like I'm taking the bus again. Christ, that means I have to go back through that shit hole Catania. Whatever. After imbibing 2 liters of wine around various city centers I get myself on public transport ("publitran" I like to call it) moving east. After about an hour the bus drives onto the ferry from the island of Sicily to the toe of the boot of mainland Italy. They sometimes refer to Sicily as the soccer ball getting kicked into the ocean by the boot of Italy. I can see that now. It's a relatively short journey considering you can see the land mass divide from space. It feels like I'm moving between two different worlds. And so I day dream in the Mediterranean moonlight.

When they have you locked in the nut house, especially in solitary, every precaution and safety measure is taken so that you don't have the ability to hurt yourself, hurt someone else, or escape. Then usually after a few days, weeks or months they let you out. Most people, myself included, find themselves locked right back up again in no time. It's a tough situation. When you get committed, you didn't necessarily commit a crime of any kind, so there's no timetable for release. They don't let you out until the doctor says that you are rehabilitated enough. Part of that is accepting that you are nuts. So if you weren't nuts on your way in, you have to get nuts and admit it before they let you out. There's no need to rush the process though because most likely you'll be back in the loon bin in no time.

The journeys that land me in those place these places are always interesting and unique, but the destination is the same every time. The funny farm is not unlike hostel life really. Wandering vagabonds sitting around communal space speaking incomprehensible words. Bunk dorms full of weirdos trying to fill you with all sorts of ideas. Everyone taking different colored pills all day. The place feels like a romparoo, especially when some guy wearing pants on his head interrupts your activity to preach about god or aliens. I've accepted that these flashbacks are always going to be a part of my life, and most likely death also. That just seems to be the way it's going.

I wake up and look out the window - the sun's almost up. Where am I? Did I make it to Lecce yet? The guy in the seat next to me is also looking around and trying to figure out where the heck we're at. I get the feeling we missed our stop. It's always hard to tell on this type of publitran, especially if it's your first time in the area, don't speak the local language, and were too lazy to set up international cell service on your smartphone. I think I unintentionally handicap myself in this way just for the challenge.

Well shit. As best I can tell, I and my new American companion were supposed to get off at the last stop 50 kilometers back. My Italian linguistic skills are a little sharper now that I've been in the country for a week and am out of the Sicilian dialect region. I think the bus driver is telling me that he's continuing to the east, but that he has can drop us at the next station and a bus will be by soon to take us back to Lecce... I think that's what he said.

In America, we basically have two types of buses - public buses like Greyhound, or school buses. A lot of times when you're riding buses around foreign countries, everything is a school bus. So we weren't surprised when that's what pulled up. Cool. It looks like we have the bus to ourselves, and Lecce isn't too far away.

Andy from Cincinnati is basically backpacking around just like myself. He's just as lost as I am in life, but with a better excuse since he's about ten years younger than me. His packing skills suck. He doesn't just have a backpack, he has luggage man - like a duffle bag with wheels. What the fuck is he carrying in there? Rookie mistake - less is more junior. Oh well. The sun is barely up over the horizon now, and the bus comes to a stop. Three kids get on, and in a completely empty bus decide to sit right the hell next to us. Totally unnecessary. They're checking out our bags, and can clearly tell we're out of place. At the next stop, they convince us that we need to stow our luggage under the seat. I've never been to this region, but from what I remember of Italy fifteen years ago when I was studying abroad in Rome, kids often pull pickpocket type schemes on tourists that are out of their element. Who could blame them, it's an easy grift. I don't feel like arguing, so I play along. Andy follows along as well but has a more awkward task because he's carrying a lifetime supply of possessions apparently.

After a dozen more stops we come to realize that the school bus we are riding on is actually a school bus taking kids to school from the outskirts of the city. 45 minutes later the vehicle is jam packed with a thousand kids hovering over us like we're unicorns in a petting zoo. One of the cool kids from the first stop is now making me do his English homework that's due in an hour. Ha! I'm happy to help, but god damn, their understanding of English is way better than half of America's high school youth these days. They are tricky linguistic exercises even for me. Maybe this whole aspiring writer thing isn't for me after all. Good times though. The bus driver lets us off somewhere on the city outskirts before he gets to the school.

After an experience like that, I feel like sitting down with this fellow at a bar and replaying that ridiculous series of events over a couple beers. But it's breakfast time, everyone is on their way to work, we're basically hobo immigrants, and I have to take a shit something fierce. Ok bro, nice knowing you. Hit me up or whatever, I'm headed to Umbria Street or something like that. Holy shit, I need a bathroom fast!

Well, Lecce is a pretty cool town. Great food, cool nightlife, architecture, history, art. It's clean and inviting with the kind of locals that make you want to spend a lifetime or two here. God, I love Italians.

After a couple pleasant days, I move on to Gallipoli. It's as beautiful as pictures on the postcards (my main compass for where to go next lately) but the place seems pretty boring. It's windy as hell and the beach feels like Atlantic City in November. Empty. I should get up and explore, but instead, I decide I need to take refuge in my hotel room for the day.

I think I'll always be the same age, 23 I guess, something like that. I stopped aging a long time ago. I think maybe, hmmm, what is this mindset? I guess I'm on vacation now, but I suspect this lifestyle will be the way it is for a while. Life has opened this door for me. A lot of things had to line up and fall apart to make that happen, but I ain't really mad about it I guess. Looking forward, the ideal situation I think is that I somehow end up happy with a young beautiful wife, have a couple kids, stable job, poker friends, and a nice house in a nice neighborhood in a nice town. And then I settle into the easy chair and watch the kids and sports and movies. I have great sex with my very loving wife and play video games with my kids and their kids. And that's all. These things are all well within the realm of possibility, right? I'm pretty sure that sort of thing happens all the time. I'll need a relaxing job where I make a lot of money though. I basically have that now... I'm really close on this.

All packed and ready to go from Gallipoli to Otranto. I check out from my room and tell the owner of the hostel my plans. He's got bad news. It's some sort of holy holiday and the trains aren't running today. A fact that is reaffirmed by the bells that have been ringing all around town nonstop for the last two hours, and the procession of people carrying statues of the Blessed Virgin Mary around the streets. Luckily he's able to hook me up with a gal that's driving that direction today anyway, so I hitch a ride. She just asks that I cover gas money. I agree, but give her double for her trouble. It's funny, nobody tips here. For these people, especially in the rural parts, tipping is looked at as odd as some stranger just handing you money. Sometimes people try to say no and give it back. Sometimes they can't believe their great fortune of having received free money. I like to give it away anyway. Why not, my banker won't notice. How could he, he doesn't even exist.

Otranto is another small coastal town on the Adriatic - the east coast of the boot of Italy, down by the heel. It's pretty nice weather for walking around in, soaking in the surroundings, and feeling the history in the castles and ancient ports. Breakfast at a tucked away cafe, pizza for lunch and my first couple glasses of wine looking out over the water. I guess I've basically been rolling around solo for the past week or so. I'm getting better at the language since I don't have much more to do to occupy my time in these places than overhearing conversations. I'm a loner Dotty; a rebel.

And then my old familiar friend returns... lo deprecione - the depression. Mild though you are right now it is nice to feel normal. Riding high or even steady can be exhausting. But with your aid, I'm all caught up on sleep. I stay in for the night and watch a stupid movie and cry my eyes out for no reason. It was basically a comedy film. Where am I, and what the fuck am I doing? These are good questions to be asking yourself at this point on a trip like this.

This state of alone is most likely where I will live the vast majority of the rest of my life. I always come back to thinking that it's just time for me to give up on this idea of finding companionship. It's just not going to happen. I'm too old and bitter. How can I convince myself to no longer be interested in being with a girl anymore?

On the opposite end of the porn star scale that turns me off, there is the one percent of pretty girls that are good and decent and true and pure basically. Not virgins, that would be a little weird, and wouldn't work out anyway. The ones I encounter are usually spoken for. That's fine, it's the way it should be I guess. I don't make a move on girls like that anyway. I'm not worthy of love from a girl like that. They're too nice for me, and wouldn't benefit from my negativity or scars. I'm a Groucho Marxist - I wouldn't want to belong to any club that will have me as a member. I'm ruined. This logic kills me. It is the thought loop that puts me in this current dark cloud. Defeated.

Geez, you should see how my dad lives. So alone. So alone it's sad. But it seems to work for him. He's crazy though. The local news is his friend. He has his lawn and garden chores in the morning, noon news, afternoon visit to the bar, more news, sports, some beer, then off the sleep. Every day. Monday and Friday should have lost meaning to him fifteen years ago when he retired, but they're still the same tick-tock of life that will drift him to the grave in the blink of an eye.

I don't think I'll end up like that, but who cares. I think I just want to go to work and play video games. And maybe hike and ski a little so that I can take a couple pictures now and then to feel like I am living a happy life. Maybe I should get a tattoo and a cat too. Who cares? Once I give up on love after this plain moon girl thing is over, I think I might just throw in the towel. Girls will like me though. They always do, but I don't like them back because I'm spoiled rancid grapes. To return their love would make the world a happier place, and I am not a nice person. It is in my nature to be cruel. I can't be happy with something that I can have, only discontent and upset about the things that I can't have. It's a poison loop. And it will haunt me all my days I'm afraid.

I can quit on the whole game, but then in one conversation find myself in the gravitational pull of another heavenly body. Like I've done a thousand times I'll move through her orbit and slingshot into the black abyss that is my natural state. I'm a cold dead meteor drifting still in space until I come near another satellite of love. Gravity tugs, but it the end we just drift by each other barely making a dent in each other's trajectory. She and I are alone just like everything else in the galaxy. This is the reality. This is the dark abyss, the dark cloud in which I will always live. Oh, but maybe I'm wrong. Maybe this dark cloud isn't the reality of this life. But right now, like so many other times of my perceived clarity, it's the truth.

Ostuni - city on a hill. A fascinating place. This is the hustle and bustle of Italy that I remember. So disorganized, so much chaos, and nestled right in an ancient town that children have been being born into and fixing and painting over and carving out for thousands of years.

I could write about the scenery, or monuments, history, art, food. They're all pretty cool, but they're just points along the way. The way is the memory of people and experiences that you bring back with you. You don't need to buy mementos and tee shirts to prove to yourself and everyone else that you've there.

I'm in some sort of wine hangout eating olives, listening to jazz, and talking with a neat guy here about.... I don't exactly know. We don't speak each other's language particularly well, but to the outside observer, we're two people having a conversation. I think we're talking about olives and skiing... not totally sure though. But we do speak the international language of darts. I throw defeat from my hand of victory. I tie for silver with all but one. My target, my target, stay still for your life. For the love of your life stay still. Or move at your chosen
106

speed in the direction of your heart's desire.

My new friend Domenico, or Menga as his friends call him, has let me stay in his apartment. It's a work of art. He works at the tourist information center. He helped me find the B&B I booked before I got on the train to this town. But when I arrived, nobody was there. So I returned to his office and he said that I could rent his flat and he'd stay with his dad for a couple days. That's Italians for ya man.

His father owns the car repair shop downstairs. Again, in typical Italian tradition, he's dressed in a clean starched uniform looking like he's running a pit stop in the Indy 500. They take great care in everything they touch and have great pride in what the produce. Menga brings me a bottle of a special olive oil that I can use to cook with. He tells me about true virgin olive oil that's nothing like the stuff you can buy in the grocery store for less than fifty bucks a bottle. Apparently, they take as much pride in the quality of olive oil as they do in wine. He offers me a bottle to take with me on my travels, but I'm worried about it opening up inside my backpack and drenching the few clothes and possessions I'm traveling with. It's a decision I immediately regret as I board the train out of town.

I'm past the halfway point of the trip now. What have I accomplished, what is left to be done? I've taken this trip. That on its own is an accomplishment. It's like swimming out to the deep end or jumping off a high ledge into deep water. It's like water I guess. Like boiling ocean water. Water that you can go under. And when you're under the water it's a home. I live in the dark abyss of an ocean of cold dark salt water. Boiling cold. My love boils with the intensity of a thousand frozen oceans. I continue to pick up momentum. Like a cold rock drifting in space past orbits. Destination, Rome. The exploration and plunder of a land discovered. Rome!

I'll be there in about 2 hours. I ditched the end of the tour of the coast that I had planned. Slow coastal life has been nice and refreshing, but as I've started to feel the buzz of a city I've only been able to think about getting to Rome. It'll be neat to switch it up from the beaches to a town that has been living in the heart of humanity for like five thousand years.

My bullet train moves along like a speed dart at 250 kilometers an hour, but it's very quiet inside, and everyone practically whispers. Most of the seats are set up in fours facing each other with a table in the middle. It would be a great place to play cards if traveling with companions.

I get up from my seat and move to the bar car. I lean back and cross my legs, watch the countryside streak by, and sip my espresso like the distinguished gentleman that I imagine myself to be for the moment.

The Big Olive

It's a surreal feeling. I'm grinning ear to ear as I exit the train station. But I must be mindful that I'm in an urban area and clearly a foreigner. I'd be an easy target to spot for any of society's parasites that feed on those stunned by the magic of the moment and the confusion of trying to find their bearings in such a city. Elements like this live everywhere around the world. I bottle my emotion and walk in a direction away from the station, but toward some sort of lit area. I booked a hotel room about 3 blocks away. After meandering a bit around in the rain past ancient priceless works of art and architecture I find my way there. I have arrived.

I think I'm getting pretty good at this. It's nice to do things you're good at. I concur towns. Veni Vidi Vici. "I came I saw I conquered". I line up these shots, and bounce onto trains and such, land in towns and work a map to get to a specific point. Then I set up shop, do my thing, and line up the next bounce. It may be hard to appreciate, but I sometimes impress myself with my speed, efficiency, and accuracy in this type of travel. You should have seen me get to a remote island in Thailand, procure a motorcycle and enroll in scuba lessons with a person that a friend from Vail told me to talk to; all within about two hours. I'm like James Bond basically. I am James Bond. 007. License to kill, pussy galore, the man with the golden gun.

I'd like to go to a soccer game while I'm out here. I've really gotten into soccer in the last year. It's a great sport to watch. I don't know why people think of it as slow. American football is my favorite sport to watch, but geez, talk about slow. Each play is literally only about 5 seconds. If it were continuous action you could watch a full came in about fifteen minutes. But that's just not enough time to consume an appropriate amount of beer for such an occasion. So yeah, I'm looking forward to watching some soccer. I'd also like to see a Shakespeare play. King Lear if I can find it. I can probably find it.

Also, I'm meeting with my cousin. We've been talking on email, and are both looking forward to hanging out. She says she has classes like 3 days per week, and a big exam coming up, but that they'll let her take time off since family is in town. I have no idea what her life is like. I kind of picture being a nun like being a prisoner. Like I don't know if she's allowed out. I mean, what do they do all day? Pray, I guess. They probably go to funerals like my dead step dad's and kneel and put on the ole "repeat after me" show. I should be prepared to talk about my relationship with Jesus. I know she's gonna hit me with the sales pitch and try to win another soul for God. I've been trying to think of how to handle those conversations when they come up. I think I'll talk about how I feel spiritual when I'm close to nature. That's my church I'll say. Maybe that'll be good enough. Or maybe I should say that I feel closest to the creator of the universe when I'm nailing two chicks at the same time and I cum in their assholes.

The topic of Don and his life and death will most certainly come up. I need to approach that very delicately, almost avoid it if possible. But it won't be possible. I'll need to embrace it with an open honest heart. Honest, like the orbit of a thousand white hot suns around the pull a mysterious black hole, at the center of which lies the answers to questions that the collective consciousness of our species couldn't even begin to know how to ask. So yes, I'm going to have to be careful about talking with young Mila.

I wonder how the equestrian order of the ark of the holy magic covenant is getting along without their Knight Commander. Have they have replaced him with a new Knight Commander? Do they have other Knight Commanders already, or a vice Knight Commander that now has moved up a notch? More likely, they solicit money from people, and tell them that with a gift of $100 they can be a holy helper and get a tee shirt, with a gift of $1000 they can be a patriot of the Holy Ghost and receive a white hat and white gloves, and with a generous donation of $10,000 they can choose a starving child to receive mail from, receive a magical mirror to look at themselves in for hours as they pray to God to pity those of little faith, and acquire the title of Knight Commander of the Equestrian order of the holy flying saucer.

The Knight Commander, ha! That just tickles me every time I think about it. I like thinking of him as a Knight Commander. I want to refer to him as Knight Commander if he's talked about. I mean, that should be ok, right? It was front and center in his obituary that he probably wrote himself. Maybe that's why the bible has that "left hand, right hand" bit about not making such a big deal to everybody about being religious and giving to the poor (Mathew 6:3). You open yourself up to getting called out as a big dumb hypocrite. Either way, I think I'd like to continue referring to him as the Knight Commander. It's the least I can do.

So yeah, I've been trying to prep for conversation with my cousin the nun. She really has been drinking the cool aid man. I mean she gave it all up for a 2000-year-old Jewish carpenter. She was pretty too. I wonder if she sometimes wishes she wasn't a nun. I wonder if she or any of the other nuns ever cheat and go out at night and get screwed. I wonder if they all do. I mean a lot of priests fuck little boys. I'm sure that nuns get their release of insanity in such ways too, right? I don't know, maybe not. Do they diddle their little beans? I wonder if they get inspected. They must. Girl parts will get rotten if they're not inspected every once in a while. I guess a nun would inspect them, right? Or maybe a doctor? Maybe that's what a Knight Commander does. The person that does the inspection must have some sort of special name. Like "the chastity guardian". What if he accidentally pops their holy cherry when he's fishing around up there for fruit? I think I heard that sometimes a girl sneezes and busts her hymen right off. That's why they sing hymns ya know.

Anyway, I wonder if Mila can come to the soccer game and the Shakespeare play with me. We'd probably get front row seats. It would probably be better than going to the Phillies game with a retarded veteran - like free parking and everything. Awe man, it would be awesome if she could get me a little face time with that ole Pope.

So, ok, got my head together again. It wasn't easy. I stopped into a church I passed along the way, I got down on my knees and began to pray. Well, not exactly. There are a lot of churches here, to say the very

111

least. Even the small ones are as big as a high school gym, and as high or higher, lined with marble and gold and priceless paintings and immovable frescos. Blah blah blah. I went into to one today, not just to look around, but this time I went in to actually get some peace. It wasn't pretty. I sat down and put my feet up on the kneeler (because I don't give a flying fuck about the rules), and I put my head in my hands and just said figuratively - *Christ, do I gotta be like that? Am I mixed up too hard or mixed up too good? What am I taking, what am I giving, who am I helping, what am I breaking in this ocean of hours I'm all the time drinking?*

Or something like that, I forget all the words to that prayer...

No, none of those thoughts really gained ground though. But it sucks that the poison headache I had is back again and it bothers me badly when I'm lying in bed. Look at their skin glow. Look at their skin laugh. Look at their skin cry. When you can't even tell what they've got on the inside. These people wrapped up so pretty in their ribbons and bows. It's the bubblegum craze all over again, man. These people made of molasses that every day buy a new pair of sunglasses. You know what you need man, and you need it bad, the problem is, you know it too good. Where are you gonna find this hope that you're seekin', this oil well that's gushin', this steamboat engine that's crackin' and bangin' and takin' your money and you think it's funny. Uncle Remus can't tell you and neither can Santa Claus. It ain't in the flipped out phonies and fifty-star generals that'll turn you in for a tenth of a penny, and before you can count to ten will do it all over again, this time behind your back my friend

... Ah, never mind, I forget the words.

I don't know how I didn't appreciate Borghese Garden more when I was living here. It's right near my old university. It's similar in size, sprawl, and placement to Central Park in Manhattan. It's beautiful. Everything is so close here. I walk probably about 20 miles each day. That's a modest amount for a person that is in decent shape that has all day, and can drink wine and beer and water and stop for espresso and fancy pizza and pasta and sandwiches all along the way. Walk out the hotel door, turn right or left - whatever you're feeling. Take a hundred paces and sit down for a snack and beverage and look at... ya know, 3000 years of history across the street. Wash, rinse, repeat. It's the perfect backdrop to figuring out the human condition. Because all these ideas central in my neural network are right here at arm's length - family, religion, history... and basically the bloody politics associated with each of them.

As best I can figure, this uncomfortable feeling is the anxiety of seeing my cousin, Mila. She's the Knight Commander's blessed niece and a nun of the order of the holy sepulcher. So all this stuff is coming to a swirl in the eye of the hurricane, except on the inside out. Like a black hole that resides around the perimeter. You know, there've been several layers of this whole thing that have jazzed up my mind. It's fortunate that I can write them down in this paper cup here and send them off to the ether, or else I'd be choking on a backed up tank of sludge in my head.

I know that Mila probably understands a good bit of my struggle. Her older sister, also a nun, visited me way back when in one of my earliest stints in a nut house - a bad one. Mila and I don't have that much in common, other than that as kids we used to hang out at family gatherings. I'd be treated like a bastard shit head at those things by the Knight Commander, and everyone saw it. They all saw how mom went along. Mila's brother once mentioned to me that my treatment was discussed by her family on a trip they took to our house for a holiday dinner. So if I were to plead my case about how much of an asshole the guy was to me, well, that would only, ya know... it's understood. It doesn't need to be talked about like that. I think it'll be best to avoid direct answers to questions about how I feel about this side of eternity. I'll stick to passive reflections like a psychologist, saying things like: how do you think... what have you... tell me about... blah blah blah. Keep the ball in her court. Resist the temptation to poke at the dead. Maybe if I'm patient and I listen, I might hear something that I never knew. Listen listen listen.

113

The other half of this is that she'll want to convert me and try to get me to go to church on Sunday and pray the rosary. Geez, what if she asks me to pray the rosary with her? Well, I don't know, might be neat to try. Maybe I'll get lucky and summon a unicorn. But whatever, this is no light reunion. I feel like I have to be prepared here. We're not drinking a beer and watching a fucking Disney movie... although wouldn't that be fun.

They Lost the Knowledge

"You know they didn't tell me he was dead right? That's why I wasn't at the funeral." I can't say that. I must avoid. It's bait for a talking point. People know things. Truth gets out. Liars will be made not by those hurt, but by those who watched it happen. Folktale style. And, this trip isn't the end. That quote need not be played, will not be played till years later… only if someone, Joe maybe, or mom is there to back up the story.

How will I be perceived by sister Mila? At some point, we'll probably appear to each other like we did as children. But we are different now. We'll look different from how we remember each other. I need to see her like she sees me - like a soul. I feel nervous like my muscles are tight and stuck. I'm twitchy. She's meeting me at my hotel any minute now. 3rd-floor cafe. I wonder if she'll take the elevator. It's a funny elevator.

The walls of the elevator shaft are just a cage basically, so you can see the cables and watch the box go up and down. When it stops on your floor there is a door in the cage to open, as well as a door to the box, so you have to open one and then the other. Inside it's just bigger than a telephone booth. As you go up or down you see the counter balance weight contraption pass in the other direction. Ah, here she is.

The day goes pretty well. We visit many churches and see some amazing art, history, and architecture. Cool stuff. She gets us backstage to many of these places - the crypts where the ancient bones of great saints reside, and places where they don't let other people go. We were in the actual bedroom of Saint Ignatius. They've kept it pretty tidy since he checked out a couple hundred years ago. His old slippers are still resting there. So tiny.

This whole town seems to have really come together in the 1500s. It seems like that's when most of the art was done, and the buildings were built. The ruins are from a previous empire. As best I can tell, between that empire and the renaissance many centuries later there was a revolution like we are going to have, and all the priceless

115

treasures were basically abandoned in a way. The following generations, having no real idea what anything was, just started pulling chunks of stone from all the churches and monuments to put together huts and whatnot. That's why it looks like a parasite ate part of the Coliseum. The parasite was us - humanity.

"They lost the knowledge", is how this guy explained it to me the other day - the barkeep by some out of the way arch just kind of sitting there. The arch used to basically be the crossroads of humanity, but now it's just over there behind the cars. 1700 years old it is. They lost the knowledge he said. Aqueducts only bring clean water if you know that's what they're built to do. But without the knowledge, those that survived after everyone basically ate each other, didn't have the knowledge to use the aqueducts. They just saw an easy place to gather stones. They understood stones.

It takes a good empire to build an aqueduct, but a short time after revolution comes decay. Knowledge is lost. The poetry can hang around though. Even if only one or two from a catalog of thousands finds its way into the folk consciousness it could be the foundation of a new age of humanity. How do you think abstract ideas of imagination like pyramids or aqueducts came from? Probably from a fairy tale about stacking stones.

A short time after wading around in the grand world in which Mila lives her life, we stop into a gelato shop and sit down like the kids we've always been and talk about things a little deeper, a little closer to home. I think I'm doing a good job actively dodging the topic of my relation with the equestrian prince. When conversation moves in that direction I say something like "putting aside personal instances that we are both aware of, but speaking more generally", and continue on whatever passively baited subject was dangled out there.

We spend most of the time talking about her situation. I'm 4 years older than her in human years, but experience-wise we are much closer. She's been through the ringer I think in a lot of ways. Her takeaway is that grace and God and whatever makes stuff happen. I think that she thinks her parents got back together because she prayed hard enough as a nun. She has very firm beliefs about divorce, annulment, remarriage, and forgiveness. I think that in a major way, her parents gave in and got back together because all of their daughters sort of started holding themselves hostage with holy machine guns. Two had gone nun, and the third was headed in that direction until as Mila put it, both of her parents, after each of their second marriages dissipated, coincidentally ended up going to the same church every day, and eventually began talking to each other there, and then sort of mended wounds and eventually remarried. And that's how miracles work. Did they give her the real story? I wonder if they ever told her Santa Clause wasn't real.

Annulment, wow, what an interesting topic for a girl in her situation to talk about. By situation, I mean basically a Ph.D. of nuns. She's a scholar in the holy capital talking about the legal proceedings of the Pope signing off on a document saying that a marriage was never real in the eyes of God. No big deal if you don't believe in any of that stuff, but to someone who's tits deep in it, it takes on a much higher level of meaning. Her interpretation is that annulment doesn't exist. She laughs at the idea. What God brought together, she says, can't be taken apart. By that logic my parents are still married, the Knight Commander was an adulterer living in sin breaking the two of the Ten Commandments wide open. Who's the bastard now, bitches?

Mila says she barely remembers the time between her parents splitting, dad remarrying, and herself becoming a nun. And then here she is, hypnotized in the order. Maybe it makes sense to enough people around her that are in cosmically equal situations to the extent that they all feel a kinship with each other in a special way that I'll never understand. I know they laugh a lot. The sound of honest laughter is what will stick with me the most from her convent.

Here's an interesting tidbit, she still likes to run. Decades ago we'd run a few miles together around Brixton when she visited because we were both always training for our school track teams. Well, she tells me she still runs these days. I ask how that goes with the nun outfit on. She says she runs in regular clothes. So I guess that means she can easily go out in regular clothes to run, walk, or whatever she wants to do. So I guess if the spirit moves any of the girls in the convent they can walk around and explore the city like any normal 30-year-old woman might. Right? It's not like they're in jail. They're just married to Jesus, no big deal. I guess that can get complicated though with Him also being his own dad - God. And He's also apparently the Holy Spirit too, who everyone always seems to forget about like the Marsha Brady middle child. Now if Jesus is being His Old Testament jealous vindictive God self, he's probably not too keen on the girls gallivanting around town without their holy robes. But if he's acting more like the Birkenstock wearing Jesus Christ carpenter guy that's friends with all the sinners and prostitutes, I guess the gals can feel a little more free to do what they want. Everyone loves Birkenstock Jesus, and not just because he does those magic tricks with the water to wine, and loaves and fishes. He just seems like a good guy to be around.

We're out gallivanting around after one of our church sessions and we bump into a guy that shouts to her "which way to Disney land". It's Halloween, so I assume that it's just some drunk old man being inappropriate, or not realizing that her nun stuff isn't a costume. He has a cigar and is walking with two fairly attractive middle-aged women dressed like ladies of the night. Turns out he's a priest. He tells us that the crypt is open in one of these huge chapels. Rolling around with Mila is like having a backstage pass. As we get back behind the scenes of the chapel on our way down to the crypt, a couple guys walk by with a basketball. They're pretty athletic looking, probably serious ballers. They clearly just got done playing. Were they just local hoodlums cutting through the building? No, they were Franciscan priests, or monks or whatever. These people live among us. Shit, I might as well be one. I don't get laid anyway. That's basically the only rule I think. Well, that and talking about how much you love Jesus, but that's just a poetic intellectual topic of conversation that goes with the garb. These robed disciples of Christ are normal people like everyone else. They watch sports and play sports. Some of them get caught fucking kids, but some of them don't. None of them seem to get caught boning hot chicks though. Think about it. There have been hundreds of cases of priests getting caught boning kids, but not one case that I know of a handsome Italian 30-something-year-old chap getting jammed up for getting jiggy with some local parishioners in the confession booth... Hmmmm

Women confide in me all the time. I'm always happy to listen with an open ear and open mind. I'm used to it by now, maybe like a shrink might be used to listening to suicide cases. Can that shrink separate her opinion of humanity from that group? It's a similar question to - can I separate my view of women from the porn gals. I would say yes, but it takes a discipline to do that. Hundreds of thousands of gals do porn, I talk and interact with tens of thousands of girls. I estimate one in about 500 or 1000 has done porn. And that doesn't even matter... that they have done porn. Ugh, I have trouble spelling this one out. Anyway, that's not the point at all. The point that I started to tell was that women confide in me all the time. Women that you wouldn't expect to tell me about affairs, or fantasies fulfilled by strangers, or scandalous preferences, or just matter of fact slutty things that they do that you would not expect certain women to say they do.

The point is that if Mila was to tell me that she has sex all the time I wouldn't be surprised. I mean I wouldn't be surprised that she told me. I would be sort of surprised that it was her thing I guess. She doesn't seem like the type. But as life goes on I find myself more and more accepting of the reality of what lies beneath the surface of the people I have come to know.

Am I a sick freak for wondering about the sexual tendencies and desires of nuns; women who entered this hierarchy of servitude when they were girls, but are now in their biological sexual peaks; women that are still women if you ignore the clothing they wear and oaths sworn long ago? This is a reality in our cities of humanity right now, and it has been since the age of the Vestal Virgins of Caesar's court. In this prerevolutionary landscape, this is certainly a part of the human condition. Just like the repression that the same institution has put on gay people for so long, there is an ocean of pent up sexuality behind that dam.

I don't get the impression that this is the cross Mila carries in any way though. She is truly who she is. I think she's landed right where she belongs. She wears it well. And anyway, I seriously doubt that with the political landscape of the family that she'd ever do anything other than try to one-up her holy roller perfection in the eyes of the almighty power of the Christ of hosts. Sorry, that was just another unnecessary literary back flip. She's great. But women are women. Their minds and motives and instincts are extremely complicated. In a lot of ways, I think they're often held hostage by their inner instincts. And sometimes those instincts motivate them to put on an air of perfection or dominance.

What do you know about girls with deep seeded psychological issues... hot girls in college liberal arts programs that travel the world all their lives with their rock star university professor father? Girls that forget their 20s, that forget years of their lives. What do you know about girls that live double lives, people that pretend to be something they're not? What do you know about women that cheat on their husbands after they decide he's not who they thought he was? Do you think that women who married God in their early 20s sometimes get wild, and live a double life with it?

What baffles me is that men in the order have the same types of transgressions, but it's more devious, it's more widely known, but they seem to get a relatively free pass for it. People were shocked when they started uncovering all the priests that diddled little kids. Heck, I knew of one in my grade school. It was an epidemic - probably still is, but for some reason, everyone seems to let the institution of the church off the hook. I mean they were tearing down statues at PSU when it was discovered that one of the coaches could have done more to report one of the other coach's dirty deeds to the authorities. He didn't cover it up or anything, or participate in the crime at all, but they were tearing down his statues and desecrating the name of the school as a whole. Whether that was fair or not, if the Catholic church was held to the same standard there would be burning buildings and lynch mobs out for blood. Instead, everyone just kept showing up to mass every Sunday so that they could get into heaven.

So priests and nuns are held to completely different standards and seem to act on their sexual repression in totally different ways. But people are people whether they're priests, nuns, coaches, or accountants. It's not a sick twisted fantasy to imagine that there are nuns out there that have a wild side. Whether it happens with Mila or any of the other girls in the convent now or in the past or future is irrelevant.

Pope Me

I wake up with a song in my head. God probably put it there for the sake of holy Mila. It's my motivation as I go through this Sunday with her. Don't speak, I know just what you're saying, so please stop explaining, don't tell me cause it hurts. No doubt. I hear the song as maybe what's in her head. It's a much better mindset than the watered down list of reasons why I don't go to church, and the hypocrisy I've experienced.

Before we meet it occurs to me that I should be on guard; that anything I say can and will be held against me. It's funny that the cops are supposed to say that to you when they arrest you. They come right out and admit right away that they'll hold whatever you say against you - like they're just waiting for you to give them a reason to crucify your ass. So don't be surprised. I never will be any more. Wounds from those I'm supposed to trust don't surprise me anymore. Unfortunately, I doubt they ever will.

The topic that I've tried to avoid comes up. It's ok though I think... I think it's ok. Yeah, it's a fine conversation. Damn, I hope I'm not blowing it here. She says she understands, and that she knows all about the past he and I had anyway. She says she's glad I confided in her and prefers the honesty to the avoidance of the elephant in the room.

She says she knows of the temper in him. She's seen it in her dad, and everyone saw it in Don, even toward his mom and wife. But Mila says that she believes everyone has good and evil in them. Then she starts talking about the Holy Eucharist, and things like that. It usually comes back to that. It is a standard answer to unknowns. I get it. She says she hopes he confessed about this stuff to get to heaven, but that we'll never know.

Mila is on a mission from God just like me. I think maybe she's accepting that mine happens in a bar, not a church. I don't wear black. I wear what I want. I relate to people in dark situations... Those people and I relate to each other, and sense each other, and help each other...

not help out of situations, but maybe help each other through and in situations. Because that's where we will live.

Mila talks a lot about these saints that convert people. I think she wants to become a saint. I think that's her goal in life. That's ok. I'm not sure what I am supposed to do here though when she tries to convert me. Should I fake it like a parent pretending the tooth fairy left a dollar under her pillow?

These churches we keep going to are pretty awesome whether you're religious or not. They're are ancient galleries filled with priceless paintings and statues, but apparently what makes them more than just a gallery is that they also have "the blessed sacrament" out on display. The blessed sacrament is a small round cracker locked in an ornate golden box that sits out on the altar. According to Mila, it doesn't just symbolize Christ - it is Christ. Apparently, a church isn't a church unless Jesus is living inside a piece of bread and is locked in a box sitting on a table somewhere on the premises. She always kneels down and prays at the box. If you're in the club, you get to eat his skin with your soul at this ceremony that the priest puts on where he turns a whole batch of crackers into Jesus. It's a great big show with lots of singing and smoke jars and bells. There's audience participation when everyone either sits, stands or kneels all at the same time. If you sit when you're supposed to stand, or kneel when you're supposed to sit you feel like a huge jackass and will be made fun of for the next month by all the other people at the show. It's pretty funny actually, I've seen it happen. If you're not in the club you don't get to do any of that stuff, and you go to hell.

I'm a man on an island. I didn't have the advocates that some people do. I've been the advocate for fellow lost souls in the past, and they've been the advocate for me many times. But in the end, I'm not part of an order or a community. I'm free from those kinds of classifications for better or for worse. I try to keep from being reliant on anyone in this world or the next. Ha, next. What a farce. A whole other country club for those that have made some sort of oath to a certain character in an ancient text at their hour of death. Well, if that's a thing I really don't give a flying damn. From what I understand about molecules and black holes and the speed of light, I've come to only believe in the present moment. And I'm really not too sure about that anymore either lately. Either way, I'll take my chances in the eternal hellfire with everyone else that was being themselves the whole time - good bad or ugly, from wealth poverty or prison.

I don't have anything to prove to anyone, I say. I tell her that I have a calling too, and I know it. She's understood over the last week that I have a firm understanding of the Bible and the Catholic religion. There are a lot of things about me that she did not know - like having a master's degree for example. Everyone knows how successful Rich has been at applying to art school again, but I guess it never really comes up that I've been doing anything other than getting thrown in the nut house and not going to church. I'm not bragging about my accomplishments intentionally for the credit. I would just like it to be known that I'm different than I've been made out to be.

In the end, we agree that god, love, life, and death have been philosophical debates that man has had since the end of time - which ironically occurred simultaneously with the creation of the universe as far as the scientific community can tell. Humans just have this uncanny knack for observing time. Without this frame of reference known as life, eternity happens all at once. Mila and I talk a bit about a silly idea like someone worshiping The Great Tree. Is it wrong for a person to keep that type of deity as their focus in life if it motivates them to be a good person and love the world that they live in? She agrees that questions about spirituality don't always have definitive answers but she references some scripture that leads her to know that Jesus is the only true God. But theology is complicated. It's almost legal I say, historical. You can't judge people of a different faith too harshly because no one can ever fully know every moment of history, people's motives, and individual circumstances. In the past, religion has undoubtedly been used as a tool for those in power. There's no doubt that the religions that exist in the world today, and the holy books that have been passed down are a product of a history that has been tainted with evil from time to time. She agrees but tells me not to

124

throw the baby out with the bathwater. A few bad apples shouldn't be a condemnation of the whole institution. In other words, don't judge the entire religious community based on a few evil historical characters or periods. Ok, but the saying isn't "One bad apple, no big deal". The saying is "One bad apple spoils the barrel". That's why I judge hypocrisy, particularly systemic hypocrisy, so harshly. If left unchecked it has a long history of infecting societies and poisoning them into a barrel of rotten apples.

Unless you're the Pope I don't think you should go around trying to be a prophet... except maybe on the battlefield in the midst of an intense firefight, while standing up like you don't care about the bombs dropping on you or the bullets whizzing by. And even then you shouldn't announce anything deep. Just make a proclamation about chow, or the weather, or space maybe. Jesus had all sorts of ideas about preaching. He had a temper tantrum in the marketplace once and flipped over the capitalist's table because they were selling birds. That's probably my favorite story. Do they have a special feast day for that? I bet this Pope probably likes that one too. He's the people's pope they say.

He looks great! The energy of the crowd is amazing - at least a hundred thousand people. And it's not even a mass. He just comes out every Tuesday to talk about this or that on the front steps of the Vatican. Mila is translating everything he says for me. It's pretty awesome because I can basically understand, but hearing Mila and the pope speak together the same words at the same time is pretty moving - especially considering the topic of his address - family forgiveness. He particularly specified that all members of a family sin against each other because we are all human. And that means that all members of a family need to be humble enough to ask for forgiveness. It's incredible because that is exactly what I have been trying to get from Mom and the Knight Commander for years. A concession or apology, something to move forward on. Never gonna happen I'm afraid. I'll send her a transcript of the address anyway. Maybe she'll be moved.

It's uncomfortable to think about people like Don or mom praying for my soul or praying for me to stop being mad at them. I'm sure they do it though. Instead of apologizing or just recognizing any harm and insult at me in the past, they cover it up with yet another layer of self-righteousness. Knowing this is the case, all I guess I can do is basically the same thing - pity them. Pity means not only do you think the way that person lives is wrong, but you also bottle it up as some helpless case to just be judged from a distance.

We're each in each other's version of hell. I told Mila that I don't think an all knowing, all loving God would sentence a person to hell. Shit happens. There are twisted freaks that do and say really messed up things. Some get so committed to the cause that they lose their minds and go past the point of no return. Some of these people are beggars - pitied and prayed for. Some are powerful leaders - worshiped and demonized.

People are coming to the point where they are having to choose between their religion and their political party. I knew it would come. I knew from the moment Sarah Palin came on the scene and said it was god's will that she becomes the vice president. That's when it really started to become acceptable for people to stop believing in evolution, and global warming, and science in general. But even the more intelligent Christians that don't buy into that crap will stay loyal Republicans because the GOP basically keeps these people in their pocket by condemning abortion so strongly. The powers that be convince many people to believe that it's immoral to vote for someone that is pro-choice.

This pope has been putting a lot of his energy into two 2 agendas these days - get people to accept that global warming is real, and get people to accept the fact that the top half of percent of humans have as much wealth as the bottom 90 percent, and that they might not be doing a great job of caring for the rest of us.

This has led the hard core Republican media like Rush Limbaugh to talk real hard against the pope lately. For years he's been warning of the Pope's evil plot in association with Obama to liberalize the world. Rush has been telling his audience for decades that his radio show is a war against liberalism. He says that Jesus was a capitalist, but that the pope is a Marxist. He's been very good at bending peoples' minds to believe his backward faulty logic. One might lightly refer to him as a bad apple. What's that other saying?... "When life gives you apples, start a revolution." Something like that, I forget.

The war on liberalism is causing a problem for millions of Christian Republicans. They're coming closer and closer to a point where people need to choose between two opposing philosophies. How long can they ignore that? Which one wins out? It seems to me that people hold a looser grip on their religious beliefs than they do on their politics. They want to win. They want to be right. The only way to be wrong about an opinion is to admit you were wrong. To pull that lever in the voting booth against the party you have been so loyal to would be to admit defeat or ignorance. It's much easier to bend your religion around that vote to fit the mold as long as you say the right prayers and eat the body and drink the blood, then go home to watch your news like a good little girl. Unfortunately, I don't believe in hell, because if I did I would be able to just say well, these people are going to hell. But they won't. At least that's something I can agree with these people on, even if it is based on completely different logic.

The two things most condemned by Jesus in the Bible are hypocrisy and capitalistic greed. Look, politics is a religion, and religion is a business. Those fucking castles of gold and marble don't build themselves. Guilt that pays for forgiveness and silence goes a long way. Always has, and always will. What that treasure pays for will be created and destroyed like the aqueducts unless we can hold the knowledge somehow. This great pope met with the highest ranking Republican in Congress recently, and the guy quit his job later that same day. The lies that have been spun for the last couple decades are coming unraveled. I'm very excited to see that deck of cards fall in on itself.

After the pope's speech Mila and I have a few more philosophical discussions. Purgatory, Hell, abortion, Catholicism, politics, and which is the best gelato shop in Rome. It's a nice end to another fine day with my cousin. We go our separate ways as the sun goes down. For some reason, she always seems to have to get back to the convent by night time. It's strange seeing a grown woman follow rules like that. I decide it's time to drink myself into oblivion and process all our time together.

And so here I sit here alone by the river of souls on the side of this side street. It's a walking ground for everyone from everywhere. Trastevere. These little town blues are breaking my heart. I want to be a part of it, in old New York. I'm just hanging out here writing my story a couple blocks away from the Tiber River in what used to be the center of the world.

Maybe it would seem like I'm sitting here with my book and pen just for the attention. But that would be like saying any of these ancient churches, priceless statues, paintings and gold ceilings are here just to show off. But in fact, they, like me, are just blending in. There are street performers, painters, poets and scribes but nobody is showing off. You'd be showing off here if you were dribbling a basketball. Basketball is for hoops courts. This art culture is for Trastevere, is for Rome. I'm a nice part of the scenery sitting here, just like the church art is a…

Holy fuck-smoke, look at that hose hound. My sex glands have been on overload in this place. My god the women are beautiful here, everyone is beautiful here, except for me of course. I'm a dog, a mangy mutt.

A martyr of reason

It looks like I should be able to see a doozy of a soccer game today. Roma vs. Lazio. I remember how much of a rivalry this is from when I lived here 15 years ago. It's one of the biggest rivalries in international sports. I was lucky to score a ticket to the game, but it wasn't cheap. Mila won't be able to come with me. She's in retreat. 24 hours of no talking, only silence thought, and prayer. I imagine that the Roma faithful will be in the exact opposite mindset.

I was hoping to get to the game early in order to experience the pre-game tailgate festivities, but transportation to the stadium is all jammed up. For some reason, the bus that normally goes to the stadium doesn't run on big game days because of security concerns or crowds or something like that. The bus driver explaining this to me is shouting at me, so I have a hard time fully interpreting. Classic Italy. So disorganized. So now I have about 45 minutes to get to the stadium a couple miles away. I guess I'll just have to take the ole shoestring express. I start jogging but as I get closer and to the stadium, I can hear the roar of the crowd and I realize I need to break into an all-out sprint. I'm missing all the action.

I can't figure out which gate my ticket gets me into, so I keep getting turned away. Fuck, they're singing the anthem, I'm gonna miss the beginning of the match. I lap almost all the way around the stadium for the next ten precious minutes until I finally find my way inside. The match begins just as I get in.

The crowd is 90% Roma fans. The Lazio fans are segregated to their own end of the stadium separated by a full section of empty seats on each side. The authorities intentionally do this for certain matches as a means of crowd control to prevent each sides' hooligan fans from beating each other up.

It's a great match, lots of emotion. With ten minutes left in the game, Roma goes up by a goal off a penalty kick. The place goes absolutely ape shit! As time runs out the place is singing their victory song, and everyone is hugging each other and grown men are crying tears of joy.

God, I love sports.

Afterward, I start my nightly routine of drinking myself into oblivion. Tonight the good times begin in Campo de' Fiori. This was a popular hangout for me and my schoolmates when I went to school here back in the day. Looks like the nightlife still draws a young crowd. It's always a party out in the square between all the clubs.

In the middle of the square, there's a statue of Giordano Bruno. The plaque on the statue says he was a philosopher, mathematician, poet, and cosmological theorist. He's remembered as a martyr for science and free thought. He was your standard historical figure touched in the head by the hand of God, burned at the stake by the priests of religion. It happened right here at this very spot where the hippies are smoking pot, playing guitar, and making out with their lovers.

Mila and I have spent four or five days together now. Churches, galleries, dinner, and a couple stops at the nunnery. At one point her mother superior even invited me to join them at an architecture class where she was a guest speaker. The topic was a Spanish architect that I know very well and am fond of. I was the only person in the class that has ever seen his work in person, which I found odd because this is a masters level class, and the subject is Gaudi, certainly one of the most famous architects in Europe. This whole time Mila keeps trying to get me to go see her priest. She said she doesn't want to force me or anything, but if I want to give a confession I could. It's like geez, what the holy fuck and a half, right? I think about going for her sake, going into the confession box, giving the old geezer a piece of my mind and telling him that if good people that don't believe in this stupid Lord of hosts all go to hell, then I'm going down with ship too, and I'll see him on the other side. Then I'd sing a bar of Alice's Restaurant, walk out of the box eat a holy host with my cousin, and let her think that she saved my soul. That's just dumb though, too much work, and they'd probably bring me in front of an ecumenical council and brand me with the Pentecost or some bull shit when they figure out my ruse.

I awaken with a rare contemplative clarity. I believe I may have freed a ghost from his burden a bit. I am of course talking about The Knight Commander. I was in mom's house. I haven't physically been in there in about 6 or 7 years I think.

I was milling about the place with a bunch of the folks that I've seen in the house over the years. I knew Rich was around but I wasn't sure where and I knew I had to keep my distance. At one point I saw him in one of the upstairs rooms - it was ambiguous whether he was a boy or a girl, but he was still bratty, so I knew it was him. My dad was there, and it was pretty weird. He was there with a girl or two. I guess they didn't know I was in the room, although it should have been fairly obvious since I was asleep in the bed... but it was the bed I sleep in at my house in Vail, but the room was my old bedroom in mom's house. I think it's called a lucid or waking dream or something like that because I recognized it wasn't real but was able to go along with it anyway. I was looking for something in her house, but I don't remember what. I was talking to her about where it might be, and which room used to be what - the house was always being remodeled and switched around, and I was trying to get my bearings on where I was relative to where things used to be. I was downstairs again when Don's twin brother, Mila's dad, walked into the room. He's usually very jovial and happy to see me, but there was an awkwardness, I guess in my dream mind he knew how I felt about Don, and ya know, wasn't warm to me this time about that. But we said hi, how-do-ya-do in a very nice way. Then Don came around the corner. Now, it wasn't his ghost... I mean it obviously was, but in the dream scenario, he was mingling with the living as another living person. I knew he was sick though. Like he was a little frail, or he carried himself as frail. We all knew he was sick though, just like he was in real life I guess. Apparently, in the actual last few days of his life he walked around knowing that he was about to die, then a couple days later he basically died in a drug-induced coma. At least that's what I've been told. I wouldn't be surprised if he's still alive and this whole thing is one of those classic "trick the bastard into the mental institution" gags.

 Anyway, back to the dream. A couple of us were downstairs in the kitchen area. Don came walking around the corner. I walked up to him and hugged him and told him I was sorry... I meant sorry to hear about his frail condition. He immediately collapsed to the ground. I was still holding him, but he fainted I guess or something, and I got the impression this huge weight was lifted off his shoulders.

Waking up the world seems different, just like the day I found out he died. Well, I guess it's back to normal now. Mila sends me a note that the gals have invited me to a funeral mass that they're giving at a giant graveyard on the northern end of town today. It's some sort of remembrance for members of this fraternal order here in Rome. I like that sort of stuff. Not funerals or church stuff necessarily, but local flavor. I only have two days left before I fly back to the states. This is gonna eat up the day with more religion, but I decide to go anyway since the universe seems to be pulling me in that direction.

The graveyard is enormous, several square miles. In typical Roman fashion, each burial plot has a headstone that's a centuries old work of art history. I'm underdressed, but there was no getting around that. I'm living out of a backpack, and everyone else is wearing handmade Italian suits. I mostly stay off to the side with the graveyard kitty cats. After the service, the gals and I are walking back to the car and mother superior has us swing by a grave that she wants to pray in front of. I don't know who it was. She's a real nice lady, very genuine. She has taken a shine to me I think. We start talking about her days before being a nun - she says she studied modern art at some college in northern Europe. That would have been in the 60's. I get a pretty strong sense that she had a wild streak in her life at that time. Just a hunch.

Mila and I decide that with our last day together we're gonna go to the Museo Vaticano - the Vatican Museum. It's a funny place to wrap your head around. It basically sits right on the north wing of the pope's castle, but among many Christian artifacts, it contains the spoils of thousands of years of conquests of other civilizations. You can almost smell the blood of infidels dripping off the ancient Greek statues. Mila appreciates the linguistics and the history of the ancient texts and hieroglyphs carved into stone but rejects the religious philosophy of worshiping many gods.

In general, she's been receptive to my ideas on faith, but only in the way that a tennis player receives the serve. People of faith usually have canned arguments that they give to people that doubt Jesus - like, what if you're wrong and you go to hell because of it. But most people don't have these discussions in a museum filled with stark evidence of flawed logic.

But she's all-in when it comes to her faith. She can't waiver. She's already sacrificed the majority of her young womanhood to her devotion. She says it's not possible to "chicken out" of her devotion to Jesus because it's God's will. She used the same logic to tell me that annulments are not a real thing. I guess that can help her perceive her parents as having always been married, but that puts her uncle Don in the precarious position of living in sin for 25 years with my dad's wife. Oh well. At the end of the day, people are going to do what they want, and use whatever faith or legal arguments they can find in order to make themselves feel justified and righteous.

Mila makes her final sales pitch, and I have to pass. She wants a "conversion" so badly. I think they get a badge for that or something. It's kind of weird at this point. She just wants to save my soul, and I'm really not into it. I put it to her like this, if the way Christianity is taught and practiced doesn't change to include good people that are not of the faith as a fixture in their heaven, then I cannot in good conscience be a part of it. "I'll go down with the ship", I tell her.

Mila and I say our goodbyes and look forward to hopefully meeting up again. I jokingly bow and kiss the back of her hand like a French gentleman as she gets on the bus. She blushes, laughs and sighs. I don't think nuns are used to hilarious jokes like that. Good comedy and goodbyes are all about timing I think.

Work doesn't start back up for another week, and there are cheap flights from Rome to New York City. I'm gonna drop in on ole Brixton. I wonder if I'll be able to make it through without getting thrown in the nut house again. You never can tell what kind of surprises that bunch is gonna bring to the party. I'm way overdue for a visit to see dad and the grandmas even if mom doesn't want me around.

It sure would be nice if someone would be so kind as to pick me up at the airport. I getting tired of publitran, and it'll be nice to have someone to ride into town with. There are enough people there not doing anything with their lives, I'm sure somebody will come through.

This month hasn't been as much a vacation as it has an exploration and an adventure. It's like hiking the Appalachian Trail or being on a competitive sports team. It should be enjoyable, but you have to work and be savvy in order to do it well. Otherwise, it's not an enjoyable experience at all. And nobody gives it to you. You have to go get it. I mean you don't have to, but you're free to try if you're so inclined. Just like you don't have to play football, basketball, run track, or play guitar. But if you have the gumption and wherewithal, why not go for it?

Meet Me in the White Room

Return to Brixton

If I had a nickel for every girl that's broken my heart or had her heart broken by mine, I'd probably be able to buy a loaf of bread. And how does that make you feel, the psychiatrist would ask. I feel fine doc, go fuck yourself. So needless to say, plain moon girl isn't in the picture anymore.

I realize something on the way back to the states. How it took me so long, I don't know. It's so simple that it actually makes me happy because that means there must be so many other simple truths hiding in plain sight that everyone else knows the day they're born. After a certain point, there is no changing people. How have I not accepted that for so long? They may hold a precious sacred position in your life - wife, mother, brother, priest, friend - but when you realize a departure in them from reason, and you feel the resistance of ignorance, you must stop short of the temptation to enlighten... for the most part. For many, once they reach certain points of their lives, turning to a new way of thought is simply not possible, even if the old way is clearly a dead end. I've known this for a long time, but have pushed so hard against it. I won't consider it a failure, just a hard learned lesson with deep roots in all its pitfalls and complications. I sure hope I don't forget this epiphany tomorrow.

I push hard against lots of things. Most are so impossibly anchored that it's silly to knowingly continue the effort. But failure feels like death sometimes. It's ok though. Failure is ok as long as you accept that it was an outcome of the endeavor. It was just an exercise like lifting weights - a lost cause that one can only hope results in strength... and wisdom. Sometimes a person gets lucky. Sometimes the gods smile upon thee and a new truth is revealed; a curse is broken. That hope of a miracle has been my motivation to push so hard against a seemingly immovable object for so long. But I'm tired now. And so is she I'm sure. The unstoppable force has met the immovable object, but I believe the fabric of time and space has stretched itself in order to allow us both to exist in each other's world.

My lesson is that instead of trying to teach the dirt not to cool or the wind not to shift, I need to accept the elements for what they are and work with them in their state. They shouldn't be the object of my efforts anymore.

My flight lands in JFK early evening. My goofy roommate from freshman year at PSU lives in Brooklyn, so I call him up to see if he wants to hang out and let me crash at his place. We stay up all night drinking beer, bullshitting about this and that, and watching Star Wars just like the good old days in the dorm. In the morning I start my publitran voyage to Brixton. The comic book and me, just us, we caught the bus.

I'm not so excited to get back to Brixton, but it's an obligation I can't defer. In general, I like to basically be able to have the option to come and go and not be really noticed if possible. Well noticed is fine, but I wouldn't want to be expected to make any kind of speech or intentional gesture. The problem is I have no real place of refuge there and no getaway car. It would be nice to be able to just blend into the events of the day, and watch or comment on them like anyone else. Of course, there will be an exclamation of hellos and what not when I arrive, but hopefully if I handle it right, I can just sort of settle in and try to answer the double jeopardy question on TV with everyone else.

Mom still insists that I don't come to her house, but she's willing to meet somewhere for lunch. I guess that'll have to do. My friend Annie the psychologist reminds me that mom is still grieving and probably still trying to be loyal to the Knight Commander and do what he would

136

want her to. It's lame, but that's the way it is right now. With this much division between us, the only thing we've ever been able to talk about without accidentally drifting into disputed waters is the weather. Even with that though she has a tendency to throw out the anti global warming rhetoric at any moment. I should be mindful not to wear anything red in an effort to pacify her paranoia that I'm a communist.

The Grandmas and Joe come along for the meal also which is great. Rich is not present, and not spoken of. I don't know who knows what about that. If it was just me and mom at a table chewing food, discussion of things that normal people talk about like current events, family, or health could quickly give way to an argument. Having the other three there lightens the mood and creates a warmer environment. Also, they're all awesome. I think mom's mom has her head together better than any of us, and she's 92 years old.

Decades ago I would observe how mom listened to Rush Limbaugh through the heavy static of an a.m. radio station. I saw right through the rhetoric then and tried to poke holes in it. But, he's the antichrist, and you have to give him credit for that. Logic is a magnet, a super magnet with a polar... axis or something. It's impenetrable by actual reality. It consumes thought and souls. Radio waves man. The stock market is made of numbers, the grocery story is made of the stock market, and the radio sits next to the microwave. Trust me, I know that sounds weird, but it's true.

I thought I could turn mom from this anti-Christ, but... well I don't know. Maybe with the help of holy Saint Mila it can happen eventually. I wonder how she feels about Rush Limbaugh taking swings at the pope. Probably doesn't like it so much. Mom probably doesn't like me talking to someone with Mila's take on divorce, annulment, and poverty... and influence.

It's too bad that one can't counter ignorance with logic. The heart steps in and pumps denial and religion from the lungs to the gray membrane. Wit, comedy, and satire will win the battlefield though. They rely on the most honest of responses - laughter. It's only after a person laughs that they might be able to process the root of the laughter in the deeper regions of their minds.

It can't be easy to cling to both your political and your religious beliefs at the same time as their central doctrines drift further and further apart. It would be especially difficult when they both have a tendency to skew truth and reality. It's as if you're drowning and have to choose between two cinder blocks shaped and painted like life preservers to save you. It really doesn't matter unless you have the confidence to say fuck it and just tread water there on your own for a while till a ship of Cruds pulls up. The Cruds have no need for cinder blocks while in the high sea. On land... That's a different story. They understand rocks.

I give a call to my good pal Ivan. I'm very eager to see the bee hive that he's been tending, and I understand that he his true love will be bartending tonight, so maybe I can introduce them to each other. He's a bit of a neurotic recluse, but also probably the most successful poet I've ever met. He wrote a famous novel once called The Mystery of the Owl, but it never got published. He was also the leader of a famous rock and roll band called The Peffun Zoo. You may have heard of them if you were at the show before he walked off stage mid-performance never to be heard again. He has a prolific catalog of recordings that would be the envy of any studio.

I give him a hard time for not picking me up from the airport since he has no job, but on the other hand, he also hasn't left the thirty-mile radius of the house he grew in for about a decade. He tells me that Rich stopped by his house a few days after Don's funeral. He says Rich had a gray pallor and worry warts about his face. I'm understanding the reason for his silence on the topic before I was informed of the death. He's a man of inaction. He sees and listens, but typically only expresses his observations through simplistic rhymes and gestures.

His farm is a magnificent oasis of nothingness perched tightly in a gap between suburban wastelands of identical houses stacked on top of each other, filled with wives and children and eggplant husbands.

138

Ivan's fences need mending, but the goats are abiding by their theoretical borders anyway. There's a baby around here somewhere. It's Ivan's sister's kid. Ivan lets the kid and his parents live on the farm. It's only fair since they own the place. Ivan also allows his parents to stay with him for free in the house he grew up in. The plans for Ivan's laboratory are mostly complete, but the barn needs to be built first, and the human skeleton has yet to be delivered. The weeds on the dirt pile seem to be coming in nicely. The roosters sound healthy, but they have not yet wandered back from the neighbors' houses.

I spend some time with Dad. Like mom, our conversations rarely drift far from light topics like the weather, but for different reasons. He didn't even ask me about my trip to Italy. Like mom, he has said that he has no desire or intention to visit me in Colorado either, but again, for entirely different reasons. We can watch sports next to each other though, so that's great. He's a good man with a good heart. He's a simple man taking refuge from a complex world until his lifetime passes by. He's mostly alone in his life, but not alone in his condition and approach. He's a dormant specimen, and that's just fine. If he's happy, I'm happy.

I roll the dice on another meeting with mom. A painting class, just the two of us... and the fifteen other women in the room trying to form a resemblance of some sort of abstract mountain scene while they cooze over the handsome art instructor telling us all about the color theory that he learned about in art school but is not going to bore us with. My painting sucks. Hers is ok because she colored outside the lines that the instructor was blabbing on about. I wouldn't say it was a bonding experience necessarily; more like a team building exercise, or group ice breaker. But it was something. I think we both breathed a sigh of relief when it was over.

139

Ok. I've had enough of this nonsense. *The mountains are calling and I must go.*

How to Ski

A big early season blizzard rolls in. I'm riding my ancient snowboard on two feet of fresh powder. Free refills all day - meaning you can ski the same line twice in a row, but it's dumping so hard that your tracks are already filled in by the time you take the chairlift back up. I'm way out in one of the back bowls of the mountain in a blizzard in a desert of snow. My beard is a solid piece of ice. The wind almost takes me down as I'm standing up strapping into my bindings. Visibility nil. At times the snow is so fresh that in this white out I lose reference to all senses and become unable to tell if I'm flying down the mountain, or standing completely still... until I wipe out, cartwheel a couple times, and come to an actual stop. I still can't see anything, and standing up in several feet of fluffy snow is a tricky maneuver with the board strapped on, but I dig myself a little hole, and sort of pop myself to the surface, point my board down the mountain and cruise further into the abyss. It's so peaceful in my white room.

Riding powder is like floating on a cloud. On days like this, you can get wild and huck your meat off cliffs with less regard for sticking the landing because you're just going to tumble in soft snow and then bounce back up. I've found that powder is more work on skis, and I don't come out here for a workout. I always get one anyway, but just as a side effect of having fun.

I'm a rare breed on the mountain in that I'm just about as experienced at snowboarding as I am at skiing. Barely average by Vail standards, because these folks have all skied thousands of days in their short lifetimes. Compared to the average tourist, I guess I'm pretty good. Being able to ski and snowboard makes the whole experience much better I believe. It gives me a whole extra layer of doing what I feel like - which is what the sport, and really this whole mountain lifestyle is all about.

I usually look at what the weather has done in the last 6, 12, 24 hour, and 3 day periods. I gauge the rise and fall of the tide of tourists in town at the given time. Depending on sun, wind, snow, and human density I'll choose which gliding apparatus I'm going to strap to my feet.

For me, the best part of skiing is the scenery. On clear days you can see a hundred miles in every direction. You're often looking down on the clouds with your feet firmly planted on the ground. The air is crisp and pure. The thermometer often says it's below freezing, but in the sun you feel like you're strolling on the beach. I like to just get up there and cruise on my skis on days like this.

Oh, but when the blizzard comes through, it's a whole different experience. The town is electric with excitement. Dumping, pooping, puking, nuking, powder day, chowder day, shittin sideways - all terms to describe white-out conditions.

Once I get to the mountain - I spend all day deciding where to go at my whim. This decision-making process is centered more around the soft arts of the mind. Do I want to be in bumpy terrain, remote, steep, meandering, fresh, packed, groomed, bright, top, mid, bottom? Whims galore.

Do I want to try to meet up with people and mob around the mountain with the day's squad? It's nice to ride with friends, but not always easy. Easier than last year though as my skills have improved. This is only my third season on skis. I'm just as happy to wander the mountain aimlessly by myself. Maybe I'll listen to music, maybe I'll just listen to the wind like back in the old days when I would run ten miles a day. Maybe I'll drink some beer or wine on my way up the ski lifts. One or two loosens up my inhibitions, and I think makes me better by relaxing me and taking the edge off. After 3 or 4 though I get sloppy and dumb. If I meet up with friends and hang out on one of the decks overlooking the planet, I'll usually smoke a little pot. That doesn't really help my skiing in any way, but it opens my mind and helps me appreciate the moments differently.

I barely work anymore, just enough to pay my bills which are very minimal. So this Colorado ski departure is basically just a continuation of my European wanderings. I'm still meeting random strangers from around the globe and swapping quick life stories on our 4-minute rides up the chairlifts. It's quite natural to tell the person beside you the story of how you came to be dangling 70 feet off the ground before you part ways never to see each other again except maybe on another ski lift. But even then we will have all taken 500 ski lift rides since the last time, so if you do realize you recognize this person's life story you might just sort of say, ah yes. Then ski away again. Or just realize it straight away and say nothing. Maybe take a sip of the beverage you keep in your coat, or adjust the song on your iPod, or text an acquaintance about meeting for a drink later or find a squad to meet at the top of some impossible peak to barrel your bodies down the hill at the speed of fire. No big deal. This is just a leisure activity that involves sitting on a chair lift for a few minutes, then standing on your chosen equipment and moving down the hill at a velocity determined by friction or lack thereof, slope, turn radius and frequency. It's quite fashionable these days. You should look into it.

Living the way I do now, it's hard to believe that it's been 10 years since I was last released from a detention center. There's no way I could have imagined that this would be my future. I was on the verge of suicide at that point - the ugly aftermath of running through the gauntlet of psych wards and jail houses with all the other misdemeanor outlaws.

It was around December 2005 that I moved into that house in Manayunk. I was very close to suicide. I even went to a handgun store in North Philly. I got nervous though when the lady asked for ID and asked if I had any history of mental illness. I don't think they can deny you a gun on those grounds anymore... I don't know. But I was close. I stopped answering calls from parents. Nobody else called. Except for my cousin JB once. He said, "man you don't sound good at all". Then we hung up and I didn't see him till the next family occasion a year later. One cold wet day in late fall I walked into Wissahickon Park with a rope thinking I'd hang myself. It was a pointless activity. Really, I guess I just needed some fresh air and a dramatic confrontation with myself.

143

There wasn't a tree great enough to climb up, so I continued down the path till it wrapped back around to my stupid little apartment on Ridge Avenue. I'm kind of like an old shoe sometimes. I'll just keep on steppin.

I went for another walk that night and ended up on the dance floor at one of the Irish pubs on Main Street. Standing there, snapping my fingers and bobbing my head to the beat of whatever song was popular at the time, it occurred to me that nothing of significance ever really happened. Ever. And then I made my way to the mountains five years later, and then to Thailand a few years after that where I met my Lee. Then we parted, but now she tells me she has a few days off and wants to come visit. Come to me, lover.

Explosion imminent

I'm having a drink at my coffee spot, enjoying a fine Hemingway novel - The Winter of our Discontent. My Lee calls me to tell me her bus is pulling into the Vail transpo. When I walk up the stairs to the platform I see her on a bench across the lot. She walks across the drive with her suitcase, wraps her arms around me and hugs me for quite an extended period of time; like a minute maybe. Doesn't really say too much. I guess I'm not used to affection like that, but I like it. I like it a lot.

We throw her suitcase in my truck parked next to the bus station, and take a walk into the village, through the village, around the village to a different village and up the hill to the intercontinental snowboard competition that happens to be in town this week - the Burton US open.

The weather is beautiful - hot almost. It's February in the high Rockies, but I'm in a tee shirt and she's left her coat in the truck. It's a bizarre slice of climate we live in here. We continue our stroll around town, poking our heads in a few shops and galleries. It's as casual and natural as before - feels like she never left me. We run into a few friends along our walk, and I'm happy to make introductions. It's kind of hard to believe that a peach like her would come all the way out from Florida to see a plum like me.

Her overnight travel is catching up with her, so we drive back to my place so she can relax and maybe take a nap. As she's laying there we sort of cuddle up, then "necking" as they used to say in the old times; although I'm not sure what that means exactly. I do that funny trick where my boner is rock hard so she takes off her clothes, then I'm half hard but still enough to have some sex figuring it'll come back to life, then I pull my flaccid penis out of her body so that everyone can have a good laugh. It really does make a guy want to commit suicide if he finally gets to lay naked with the gal of his heart's desire, but his boner never shows up. The pits man, it's the pits. In this case though, it doesn't really bother me because she's here all weekend and already knows I can bring the ruckus all up in that business when things get going.

Well, what should we do with the day now that we're all reacquainted and rested up? It's late afternoon and shaping up to be a glorious sunset. We walk over to the base of the mountain and hop a gondola up to the top.

There's a deck nearby with a great view of the planet Earth. Wouldn't you know it, while we're up there we stumble upon a fun crowd of people in the trees... because that's normal out here. We chat it up with my friendly friend Kyle about who-knows-what for a while, smoke some drugs, then walk back to the restaurant at the top of the gondola where we dine on seared tuna and pot pie and have a couple beers. Not much to say about that except that we end up having sex in the gondola on the way down from dinner. It's casual. The dinner I mean... and also the physical act of love. In the time it takes us to descend approximately 3,000 feet to the bottom of the mountain I put my half erect penis inside of her body as a joke. She thinks it's funny, and so do I, I think for the same reason. Descending the mountain, looking out at the lights below, the passing trees, the stars above the mountain tops in the distance, and the back of Lee's head is an image I hope I never forget. It's as etched in my memory as our rendezvous in the seas of Thailand. With very little effort on either of our parts, these things just sort of happen. I guess we're just a pair of exhibitionists. We like to get frisky in public places - hidden in plain sight.

As we exit the gondola I'm positive that the attendants know what debaucherous carnal acts we've just performed. But then I think it must be assumed that every couple getting off the gondola probably just got each other off in the gondola. Either way, I'm going to make an effort to do that more often.

On our walk over to the concert, we pick up a few shooters of wine to imbibe as we boogie to the dub stylings of DJ Griz. After about an hour, our wine supply runs dry so we pop into an interesting bar on the other side of the skating rink behind the stage. The place is sort of a

146

fusion of an upscale cocktail bar and a bowling alley. It's called "Bōl" with a line over the o. It's a fancy place. Before too long, my Lee becomes weary, so we egress to my abode.

Would you like to know how romantic I am? We're laying there in my bed, taking turns picking out music to listen to, doing fun things in the nude, and drifting in and out of sleep. Suddenly I wake up in the middle of the night with the realization that there is a massive turd that wants to jump out of my butt. Explosion imminent. My bathroom door is thin and pretty close to the bed. I don't want Lee to hear my ass blast and run back to Florida with a lackluster impression of my sexual performance and gastrointestinal fortitude, so I steal away into the night to the nearest public toilet. It's housed down three flights of stairs on the other side of the parking lot from my building. Putting on shoes is no easy task for anyone with a full sack of shit in their lower bowels. There's a moment of panic as I scoot myself across the lot as I think that maybe the door will be locked. But the gods are with me this day, and disaster is averted. The moral of the story is that my darling Lee may never know the hurdles I'm willing to climb or the ends of the earth that I would run to in order to make her happy. This is the tale of my turd of romance.

I awaken with a new found vigor and physical prowess. After a wonderful bout of sex and a shower and more sex, we emerge from my love den penthouse. It's pretty early by my lifestyle standards still - probably around 9 am. She sees my journals sitting on the table. She recognizes them as the ones I was writing in when we were in Thailand. I tell her she can bring them with her to the coffee shop if she wants to check them out, but that she might not like what she reads.

She knew back then that she hurt my feelings, and that part of the writing was a therapeutic way to get past things. She's understanding about the words I wrote such as "fuck that bitch" because even in those passages I acknowledge that I'm just saying these things in an effort to get over her absence and move on.

147

She's surprised when she gets to the part about "the young jewess, and the even younger Kiwi". She didn't know that I was with another girl right before her on that trip. So there we are sitting in my Vail coffee shop, reliving that trip, and continuing to understand each other that much better. I think she has a good bit of sex with random people. Probably a little more than I do, but I don't think by too much. I do remember her saying something about how she doesn't really believe in monogamy. An interesting approach for a girl still living with her parents.

We spend the day watching some more of the snowboard competitions, ducking in and out of the pubs, and randomly meeting up with my friends swirling around town. I like the way she talks. I like to listen to her. I like the way some of her words sound, like "funny" or "money" or "honey". Long n, long e. She doesn't say outrageous things at all, but nothing she says is really predictable. She's had an interesting life, and her words come from an interesting perspective.

The weather makes its standard dramatic shift, and by night time we're in the middle of an awesome snow storm watching another outdoor concert. We smoke some random pot that's being passed around. We get all sorts of freaky right there in the middle of the crowd, but nobody can see because we're all wrapped up in jackets, and everyone is so close that you can't see your neighbor below the shoulders. To the folks around us, we are just a couple love birds moving to the beat. We laugh and laugh, and I think maybe she came a couple times or at least came close. I'm not sure, and it really doesn't matter.

My lesbian friend that collects crystals heard that my lady is in town and scored us a couple tickets to a VIP party in the other village on the other end of the mountain. The snow has let up and the bright Colorado Rocky stars are out. She says that they're brighter than any she can remember ever seeing in her life. We walk down a road I had never taken before that passes by all the mega mansions. We're lost, but she doesn't care. We get found, get into the VIP party, get a few free drinks, leave, next bar, then the next, then the next.

148

Before the night is through I take her to one of my favorite gazing spots. Laying on the ground under a fifty-foot high evergreen tree that's strung with Christmas lights we gaze up into its branches, we cuddle, and we laugh our heads off.

Sunday. We get up early and go to church to say prayers begging forgiveness for our sinful lives. Just kidding. We sleep in, bang (or make love maybe, not sure), then go to a pot shop to get her some goodies for her trip back to Florida. I'm talking about weed man, ya know, drugs. Yeah, we have some real nice establishments out here and I'm happy to give her the tour.

About an hour before her bus leaves for the airport I decide that I think I'll tell her I love her. I don't know, I just sort of feel like it. It's one of those decisions/instincts that just sort of happens on its own, and I'm in no position to second guess it, even if it means getting myself in trouble.

There's been a lot of passion between us this weekend. Snuggling up, getting close, holding hands, embracing, kissing on the sly. And since that first day, we really have had some amazing sex and lots of it. But then we switch right into casual mode, enjoying nice days together, just like in Thailand. We really are kindred spirits. It was as obvious then as it is now.

There's a magic to meeting someone on the other side of the planet, then reuniting in another paradise. It's not just because of the places... well, sort of. People go to far off places because of a love of adventure. We meet up for a love of sharing that adventure together.

"See you soon, I love you"

"What!?!?"

"Like you didn't know... I'll see you soon though. Vegas I guess, or Colorado, Bali, whatever. Till next time"

149

"You're so casual about what you just said. You know I'd stay if... We",
"I know"

My mind is in a bubble as I watch her bus pull away. I'm disoriented thinking about the way this weekend has developed. There's a lot to process. It's been one of those happenings that I wouldn't believe unless it actually happened to me, or I was there to see it. She calls me an hour later to thank me again for an amazing weekend. She says said this weekend was "a mind fuck but in the best possible way". I tell her I'm sorry if my words scared or intimidated her, but the moment just kind of took me away. She says it caught her off guard. She wants to meet up again soon but doesn't know much more.

In the meantime, we're both two swingin singles in our prime. Late 20's for a girl is sort of crunch time. I imagine that as she considers prospects for her future, a life with me is in one of the possibilities she's considering. Same for me, but I'm in a different situation. Obviously. She'll be having to make a move out of her parent's place. My guess is that there's a garden of Jewish eggplants that are courting her, and that she has a few side pieces that she plays with whenever she pleases. Because she can. She's a very pretty girl... or should I say, attractive woman. She's not socially aggressive, but she is certainly not shy. She's smart, and she takes what she wants, what she believes is hers. I would say that in 6 out of 10 alternate universes we end up living happy fulfilling lives together and making beautiful children. She took one of my Thailand journals with her. I'm glad.

You know what's fun I think - fishing for dust. I just did it accidentally and it was great. Go sit somewhere, or stand still, in an empty still room. And stare in the general direction of a wall or a door, anything really, as long as everything is basically still. So at this point, your line has been cast. And then, just like normal fishing, you wait. And eventually, a piece of dust will float by. It's magic. It's a dust of the universe coming past your existence.

150

She only took one picture the whole time she was here. There was an oil painting station set up in one of the ski villages. She took a picture of the paint-splotched and spilled on the board… the what do you call it?... easel, no, that plate where you mix the paints to make your color. She just took a picture of that. Memories. I guess she also took a picture of an empty ice skating rink at night. Interesting little bird, my Lee

So my lady love has come and gone away, but I think she'll be back soon. I can only imagine that we are deeply in love with each other. I think we're embarking on a love affair. I can't imagine what else this would be. Lots to sort out I guess. Worlds have collided. As with all my love interests, I'm sure that we either will or will not "end up together" whatever that means. Impossible things become possible if we just let them, that's what it means. Or maybe I've fooled myself again for the millionth time. Hard to say. But when it comes to anything - anything happens, anything goes. There are no rules. In reality, parking lots don't even have stripes.

Pop

My mood improves from a week of deflation, and I have a somewhat productive day. I can't remember what I was feeling bad about or sorry for, but it's still there. I think it's the stress of an unknown coming my way. What will I do for the month of May? Where will I live in June? What will I do for the end of April when I have no work, my lease ends, and the whole town empties out? Pack, camp, and enjoy the sunshine I guess.

This sort of uncomfortable feeling has its purpose. I've always gotten this sort of feeling at the beginning of a school semester, or when I need to make a life change into the unknown. It's sort of a motivation to know that the most effective way to deal with the stress is to tackle the issue. Like if you can't breathe underwater, you're motivated to find a way to the surface sooner rather than later.

There are many tubes to take to that surface though. Maybe a road trip around the dessert for a month, maybe into Vegas to meet my Lee. I guess we'd eat psychedelic mushrooms and go see a circus show. Or whatever. Driving around the country and camping for the month of May would be cheap and nice. I think Cuba is cheap and is probably also very nice. And it would be another adventure - the kind where I like to swim to the deep end and back just to try to do it. But usually, when you get there it turns out that it's actually a nice place to play around and dive down in... Literally and figuratively

On my weekly phone call to dad, I take a departure from the normal topics of sports and weather to let him know why I won't be coming back to Brixton this spring. I tell him I just don't trust the judgment of people that continue to feel justified assessing me as an insane person. He says that he knows he did the right thing by locking me up back then and that if he thought I was in danger of hurting myself or others he would do it again. And I reiterate that that is exactly what terrifies me.

152

This ridiculous bias that the people of Brixton have toward me is clearly as strong as ever. After a decade, what level of group-think does the whole crowd of friends and family hold on to in order to convince themselves that I'm a threat and need to be kept out of the loop of something like the passing of the Knight Commander? Anyway, I'm still not allowed at Ma's house, and as far as I know, Rich still feels justified hunting me down as an enemy of his family. Who knows though, maybe he's in jail and nobody has told me. Maybe Brixton has been swallowed up by a sinkhole. Who cares.

My life is in a good place right now, and I can't risk being ambushed again if someone has the opinion that I did or said something weird and it lands me back in the nut bin. I know it is a paranoia and a traumatic anxiety, but it is also very based in reality of something that has happened many many times, and something that could easily happen again - with catastrophic outcomes. A man like me turns into a wild animal when cornered and caged with nothing to lose. How dumb would I feel for going back there if I ended up ripping someone's throat out if they tried to lock me up again? It's not a very hard maneuver. The throat and jugulars are very exposed vital organs of the human body. I can't help that I know that and am stronger and quicker than most people. I can, however, avoid putting them and myself in a position where that knowledge would come into play.

I tell dad that I wasn't kidding around back then when I would say "when you lock me up, you push me away". It wasn't some joke. I was never as crazy as everyone made me out to be when they would lock me away with no rights and no way out. "I was hung down, brung down, hung up and all kinds of mean, nasty, ugly things" as they say in the business. I was sane on the hour they pushed me down that road, but if you put a tiger in a bowl of noodles he's gonna lava lamp man, and it's not gonna be as groovy as it sounds. Of course, I don't tell it to him like that. When it comes to verbal communication I tend to speak in plain sane boring English for the most part.

He is clearly saddened but says he hopes I feel better having gotten that off my chest. Good words pop. I remind him that any day of any week he could take the three-hour flight out to Colorado if he wants to meet me. I have no intention of tip toeing around this for the next 5, 10, 20 years. I have ripped the tape off. This is the reality of the situation. I went into the conversation with the notion that I'm not going to let our relationship deteriorate into the long drawn out guilt trip dynamic that mom and I have. The timing is right in my opinion.

My spring travel always gives him a chance to passively suggest that I'm a bad son - like in that "Cats in the Cradle" song. I think that song has always been his martyr anthem. But yo, c'mon, get off the fucking couch and make something happen if you really want to have a face to face relationship. You don't have to be a baby about everything. Man the fuck up dad. You're in your 60's, not your fucking 90's. Anyway, I suspect that things will easily go back to normal and we'll talk again in a week about the weather and the basketball tournament that I'm not really watching. Maybe things change, but in all reality, probably not. Either way, I've said my peace and am fine with whatever outcome follows.

Hugs and Guns

People in Vail exchange hugs all the time. I certainly have the wind taken from me several times a week when my big boobed friends give me a squeeze. And I'm not talking about some lame emotional thing - I'm talking about how their boobs actually press against the area between my stomach and chest and constrict my breathing a little. Men hug all the time here too. I've probably hugged ten men already today in a completely heterosexual, nonsensical, and routine fashion. We're all dressed in costumes, drinking, doing drugs, being weird and flying down the mountain at dangerous speeds because it's "gaper day" where we all dress in 70's gear and pretend to be idiot tourists.

Down at the base, we bounce from bar to bar, before ending up back at our little condo complex where we barbecue then hot tub for a while before I peel off and play myself some classic Dungeons and Dragons style video games to relax my mind. Just another day in paradise, as they say.

A casual day like this couldn't happen in a million years for most of this world's population. It's a rare thing, and I make sure to try my best to cherish it like I should. Most people here haven't been to the other side where you sit at a desk, and your boss sits at the next desk over except his has a door or a window. And you both aspire to that next level that involves maybe a new title on your small business card, or a different assumed uniform - maybe a tie or an interesting hat.

I'm walking home in the dark after a long day of drinking and I come up through an outside hallway in one of the neighboring buildings to my condo. It's very pleasantly cold out. In my head, I picture having a heavy machine gun to shoot at the stone wall beside me. But I wish it was a wall that I built, very finished, but with heavy mortar that I created myself out of grit I had harvested and stones I had turned up out of the ground all through the year. And I wish that I created all the fictitious bullets that would burrow into this abyss. No, that's not practical. I don't have the imaginary patience to produce brass casings.

155

I modify my fantastical wish to just be able to pour the gunpowder into the brass casings that I had mailed to me from China. I envision that each one of those bullets blasts away at the stone wall spraying debris everywhere, and I was standing at such a close range that many of those shards of stone and metal rip through my skin; only peripheral flesh wounds since my giant machine gun that I also imported from China is basically blocking my vital organs.

I guess I had been thinking about people wishing ill will on me today. I was thinking about people condemning the devil after he was cast down into hell for challenging God's opinion on the infallibility or fallibility of man. Who cares which at this point. It's a moot point. We all know who the bad guy is. Everyone forgets that in the book of Genesis those 2wo used to be best friends… just like everyone forgets that Darth Vader was the ultimate hero of Star Wars. They had a pretty bad falling out I guess and now the half brotherhood of mankind has to live in a divided house. Thanks a lot jerks.

It's cold out there today. 3 feet of snow in the last 5 days. Gonna be below 10 degrees for the rest of the week. Negative in the nights. Then sunny and warm next week - practically tee shirt weather. I guess I'll try to get to sleep so I can wake up and get those fresh tracks. My mind is stable with a low-pressure front moving in from the void.

The thing about depression is that it can be, by definition, depressing. But sometimes you might find that you miss it if it isn't there for a while. Like Crohn's disease. I guess I've never had Crohn's disease, but I imagine if I had it and then I didn't for a while I might miss it. But I don't know, maybe I'd just be glad it's gone. I don't know because I've never had it.

After thinking about it for 4 seconds, I guess I wouldn't miss either of those things if they were gone, but I would be scared that they might come back; like a monster or someone flicking your ear, or some other thing that I don't know what it's like to have.

My New Haircunt

I have no idea where I'll be one month from now. No idea at all. I mean I have ideas, but I never know until 4 seconds before I walk out the door where I'll be going once I have nowhere to be. The apartment I've been living in for four years is having renovations done so I have to move out at the end of April. It'll be the end of an era. "The family", a rotating group of about a dozen friends, have lived there for 7 years. I don't know where I'll go or what I'll do. I'll probably just sort of drift for the month of May. I have no work that month because on April 11th the ski lifts so spinning, town shuts down and all the people leave until June. So there's really no reason to be here, so there's really no reason to pay that month of rent. So I'll be drifting. Maybe on the road of America, maybe on the other side of a jet plane ride. Maybe on a boat on a sea with my Lee.

I'll come back to Vail in late May I guess. I'll line up a new place to live. Hopefully, I can find something by myself somewhat affordable... we'll see. It might be a rough spring. That's when I get the fever usually. That's when I got thrown in the can in 2001 and 2005. Every spring I feel myself get a little electric in the head. I think maybe it's vitamin D poisoning. I drink so much milk, and when spring comes around and I shed layers, the UV rays of the sun activate a chemical out of hibernation, and I get weirder than normal. I Frankenstein like Jekyll. Electrodes scream across my mind. Stimulus. A blitz of hormones that makes me irresistible to the finer sex and a target for alpha males in positions of respected authority. It's scary. I can always tell something is coming, but I never know what. What kind of precautions does Dr. Jekyll take? The Incredible Hulk keeps several lawyers on retainer and a slush fund in his silver box. That's smart. I'll look into that I guess. All I know for sure is that in a few short weeks I'll be putting all my socks and t-shirts in my truck and turning on the engine.

Cuba may be off the board. That new virus just sprung up there, and while usually travel warnings don't affect me, instinct tells me to do something else. Man wouldn't it be nice if I felt like a normal person about going back to Brixton. But everyone is still content to drive me insane then lock me up for being insane. I'm still not allowed at mom's, and both parents have made it crystal clear that they have no intention of visiting me where I live. Maybe that's where my numb is coming from.

Then my spring deployment orders come through from upstairs. By that, I mean my human mind. Australia, New Zealand, Japan. Then South America in the fall. I just don't know how I'm gonna make it. So much free time, and an inability to stay put. Except for winter when I spend 99.9% of my time in a 5-mile radius of my house. I never even drive except maybe to the strip mall a mile down the road for groceries or a couple boxes of wine that I drink at night while playing video games.

What I really want to do with my time off is something just a little bit productive with some sort of a collective. I'm always going at it on my own. Not sure why that is. I have a comfortable truck with plenty of room to sleep in - the Tahoe of dreams. I could go back to the United States dessert. Maybe get a dog. I should get a rifle too. The whole situation really is just the perfect storm for a manic episode.

I wonder what's going on in the Brixton household these days. I wonder if Rich got married but nobody told me so that I didn't show up and go on one of those rampages they are always looking out for. He probably has a kid too. A very gifted boy, touched by the hand of God, chosen from the choir of angels by none other than the Knight Commander of the Equestrian order of the holy translucent spirit. I assume they have named the sacred child Jackson, King of Brixton, savior of the world, friend of the devil himself.

Pleasantly hungover, I'm muttering complaints about the world to myself on my way into the barber shop. I'm probably audible enough in my grief that the idiot I pass on the sidewalk can hear me. God, I hate getting my hair cut... feels more like a haircunt.

It's miserable outside today, like a woman on the rag. Snow is shittin sideways, but it's wet snow. My knee hurts from some ski related catastrophe that I'm sure I'll get over soon enough, but I have no intention of skiing over lumps of wet snow anyway. What am I, a walrus? Fuck that.

Anyway, if you were wondering if I went through with my haircunt, the answer is yes. But I was so close to kicking down the glass door and storming out in a fit of curses and rage. I was that close to being in jail right now. I'd cut my hair myself for the rest of my life, but this is my tenth one at this place, so the next one is free. I still have to go sit there and read Cigar Aficionado and listen to reruns of Bonanza and Perry Mason play in the background while I wait for the ladies to spend 45 minutes giving the 75-year-old gentleman a military grade haircut. It's the same god damn haircut General Patton's Army gave him in World War 1, but it only took 45 seconds back then. Women, always mucking it up. In the back of my mind, I realize that this haircunt is a glorious event, and the closest thing I will get to going to church anymore.

I've found that often times, the most productive and life enriching days start out like shit... like a slow wet shit that you stand up from twice to re-wipe, but ultimately make you late for work because there were two and a half more nuggets left over from yesterday's bar food. Do you remember how your day started on the day you lost your virginity? Probably pretty crumby. Mine basically started with losing my virginity because I woke up next to the girl I had been dry humping for the previous six months. We both decided that waiting for marriage wasn't practical, so we said a Hail Mary and got to it. I'm not sure if my roommate could hear us or not. He may have been asleep. He was about 10 feet away because that's how it goes when you live in a dorm room in Penn State. You lose your virginity next to the guy that was assigned to you.

So if you're guessing that I was making plans to travel to the future in Cuba with a Jew tonight you'd be half right depending on which pronouns you applied your nouns to... to which you have applied for nouns at. But that's not really important. They're all communist over

159

there, so everything should be fine. According to Karl Marx, the place should be a modern day utopia by now.

Americans aren't allowed to go as tourists, so you have to fill out a form and pick what you are. I'm going to be a journalist. My lovely Jew princess is applying under "people-to-people exchanges". I'm also considering checking the box that says "Public performances, clinics, workshops, athletic and other competitions and exhibitions". I'm pretty sure I can still dribble a basketball between my legs, so that should qualify. I'll just have to pack a Spalding. I'll be a hit over there, maybe even a champion. It really doesn't matter what I decide to tell them I am, it's just paperwork anyway, and a 4 hour sit on a plane... about as long as it takes to get a fucking haircunt in this town.

Jaryd, none other than the baby bird that used to be my roommate that laid all the chicks (as birds are prone to do) drops me a line. He lives in Australia now, and has recently published a picture that he cleverly titled "work, wash, sleep". He works at a vineyard making wine, washes in a paradise ocean, and sleeps in the forest like a hippie. So my manic idea of a few nights ago about going to the land down under will most likely come to fruition. Funny

4 pm Australia time. I should take a nap now and wake up at 12 pm America one day younger. The ninth day is soon. The ninth February 29th of my life. I can't really remember the others. I'll make a note of this one, and seal it in an envelope to be delivered on the next February 29th, 2020. With Barbra Walters. The prettiest Walters. Hey, citizens and scholars, this is how you communicate in 20/20.

One whole extra day though. What does that even mean? In between day. Still the short month though. February. It's even spelled weird. Everything about February is weird. February funerals. Now that's a hot ticket. Gloves. Don't drop the casket unless there's a hole under it. Frozen ground. Itineraries left open. Pencil it in. I wonder who the patron saint of February 29th is. Saint Tuesday. Say a prayer to Saint Tuesday, light a candle, and ring a bell. I've never been more excited

160

for a day of my life in my life.

My my my. My mind is dead. But it has a head on it still. My head. It was still because it was asleep but my thought dreams have awoken me from it. Like the sour cheese I had tonight while testing my fortune and skills of video craft. It was a fancy blue cheese, but I think it grew a foreign mold that now poisons me. I was laying here where I still lay, thinking about the metallic residual taste that I still have in the left side of my mouth where I chewed it.

I was thinking about the book, counting pages in my mind - ten pages for a dime, just another diamond mine, but this one would be all mine. And yours too, fine. Will they even want these rhymes? I was thinking how I wanted to die with a sword in my eye, because anyway, how many more times was I really gonna cry. Or maybe out the window I would fly and on the ground I'd lie, while my insides grind for a time. Maybe I'll strap on my ski and glide for a while and off a cliff I'd slide. Thoughts escaping out the side of my mind, but they have nowhere to run and hide so they come back inside. I was thinking about this guy and his bride. She could have been mine, but when she replied I wouldn't abide. I was thinking about these words again revised. I was thinking about tomorrow and the snow and the sky. But mostly I was thinking about the Jack of hearts.

Part 2

[Dear reader: This is just an abitrary midpoint]

5

Equation in the Sand

The sun's not yellow, it's chicken

What is it with North American school buses from the 80's ending up as local transport in 3rd world countries? They call it a "chicken bus" here. It costs three American dollars to take the hundred mile journey from Managua to San Juan del Sur. You gotta try it, they said. It's fun, they said... and cheap. The blazing sun has tucked behind some clouds, but somehow the bus is even hotter now. I think it's because we're approaching the outskirts of the city and not moving as fast. There's no AC, just open windows. I thought the bus was full several stops ago, but we keep picking up more and more passengers. They're mesmerized by my light skin and orange backpack. I might as well be from another planet. I think it's getting more humid now, looks like a rain storm might be coming. That would be glorious.

A few of my Vail friends came down here last week and invited me to tag along. Finding people in foreign countries when nobody has cell phone service is as fun as hide-and-seek used to be as kids just reaching that age when parents would let you outside by yourself. The boundaries then were from Adam's house to John's and the woods in between. That seemed like the entire planet back then, still mostly undiscovered. But at 6 years old that was the extent of the known world. This is more like a math problem or a Quest of the Avatar. Figure out maps and tickets and street signs as you go. Keep in mind the local currency exchange. Do your best with the language.

I see a group of drunken obnoxious college kids, so I figure I must be getting close. Nobody speaks English on this bus, and I can't see any street signs, but I decide this is the stop I should get off at. Out of the frying pan into the fire as the saying goes.

I find my way to the hostel at the north end of town where my mates told me they were staying. It's an awesome place right on the beach. The front desk girl tells me they took a stroll about an hour ago. I sign the register, drop off my pack, change out of my rancid travel clothes, and walk out to sweet mother ocean.

Finding these guys should be way easier than the time I met up with plain moon girl in Verona. That one involved several planes including a transatlantic flight, then a regional train, then local navigation to a tiny hostel in a small town. San Juan is different. The boundaries are a two mile stretch of beach and a town that really only goes back three blocks from the ocean front. They're not on the beach, so they must be at a bar somewhere. I double back on the street one block off the ocean.

Eureka! There's Joe laughing his head off, as usual, Tim leaning against the wall smoking a cig, and Plum sitting on a bucket looking around in a daze. Looks like they've made friends with a few of the locals. Joe gives a hoot when he sees me crossing the street, they reach into the bucket, and pull me out a cold beer.

Tim asks when I got here and I get to drop that great joke "I just flew in... and boy are my arms tired". Joe just about falls over laughing. The joke doesn't land as well with the locals until Tim explains the double meaning in Spanish. Plum is dumbfounded at the whole scene. The booze, sun, and cocaine have clearly crippled his senses.

I'm skeptical of this band of locals, but the guys seem to be pretty tight with them. Gerardo runs the surf shop and his parent's restaurant next door. His girlfriend is a sexy rad surfer chick from Florida. Then there's the one they call Krusty. No idea how he got the name, or what any of his weird sounds and gestures mean, but he's a riot. He knows everybody that walks by. If you walk by, and he doesn't know you, and you're a hot chick, he goes out of his way to introduce himself and invite you to the party tonight. There's a party every night apparently.

There's a kitty cat that lives in our hostel. Her name is Simba. She's a fat old girl. Lays around, walks around, talks with the three generations of iguanas around the property that also live here. It occurs to me that besides the animals, the girls at the front desk, and the cleaning woman - every other person in this cat's life passes like the wind. How could you get used to that? I've been here for 3 days, and have already seen most everyone come and go. There's a whole new set of 2 dozen travelers that weren't here when I arrived, and they will all most likely have moved on by the time I depart 3 days from now. How confusing for a cat that lives here for ten years. It must be like guarding purgatory.

Our Nica ambassadors have been more than hospitable. I'm still waiting for the con, or for somebody to be taken for ransom. Nicaragua had a terrible revolution a couple decades ago and wasn't a very safe place to travel afterward. You can still feel it in Managua - the capital. Gerardo tells me all about it while we're out at their tucked away local's surfing beach. For ten years the government power struggles led to neighbor fighting neighbor based on allegiance to either the dictator or the local rebels. Tens of thousands died. The children that were born during and after the revolution found a peace and an identity with surfing. It's not just a tourist attraction. It really is a way of life that exists outside the strife of the world, especially in post-revolution Nicaragua.

What strikes me is his description of how people have been able to let it go and move on. He says that once a peace deal was reached, people just stopped fighting and didn't talk about it anymore, even though just a month prior they had been staring each other down the end of the barrel of a gun. How does the human mind go from murderous to peaceful like that? I hope we can get to that point in our country without having to kill each other. Revolution seems inevitable though.

Gerardo invites us and his local friends over to his house and tells us to bring a fish. Ok. So Tim and Plum fetch a fish while Joe and I get a bottle of mid-day booze. His house is hot as hell, the floors are made of dirt, and there's really only enough electricity to keep the beers in the fridge cool... less warm anyway.

He wants to cook us some of his famous ceviche - a very popular dish in this region. Well, you don't really cook it, you basically mince the fish up and cure it in fresh lemon and lime juice. The acidity of the citrus basically does the cooking.

These guys are great - friendly, funny, hospitable and quite fashionable. I don't think we'd be hanging out as much though if Plum and Joe weren't buying coke for everybody. It's all good, everybody wins. It's what you do down here. In some cities, you go to museums and sporting events, here you surf and do cocaine.

Apparently, chicken fighting is pretty much the national pass time here. It's basically bull fighting for a town that can't afford a stadium. Bloodsport in a country still recovering from revolution like ours will be soon. Gerardo has five or six fighting roosters in cages in his back yard. He loves them. He hugs and kisses them, then grabs one by the feet and sort of swings it past another one to get them riled up. He's testing to see which one is going to be his champion tonight. He chooses Hero - a fine specimen.

It's a bloody affair. It's like a boxing match where the boxers are drunk and allowed to carry knives. They attach glass shards to the roosters' feet. It's a mess. They have coaches too. Between rounds, the coaches put the chickens' heads in their mouths to breath on them or something, or clean their eyes. I have no idea what they're doing actually, only guesses. Then they bring them back to the center and hope their beloved chicken can still stand. If not, you would think the fight's over, but it's not. As long as the dying chicken is still clinging to life, the other chicken just pecks at the chicken laying on the ground. Women and children casually watch from the makeshift bleachers that surround the fighting pit that's about the size of a living room. The men and chicken owners place bets on each match. Afterward, both

166

chickens usually end up dead and are placed on top of the chicken coop where the next contenders are sitting waiting in their box for their chance at glory.

Chickens are a product of human innovation and stability. They're a small ripple of chaos away from becoming extinct. Suppose that there was an awful cataclysm in our part of the world. If there was no more food on the shelf in the grocery store for a month due to perhaps a bomb or an economic meltdown or a disruption in the fuel supply etc., nobody's going to be feeding chickens in order to grow them into maturity and process them into food. Instability would wreck that chain. And occasional instability is a constant of nature. Chickens are fine for now, but do you think they last in war-torn areas? No. They're the easiest catch, the lowest hanging fruit, but they don't grow as fast or prolific as other organisms. They can't hide, and in a world of rabid hungry beasts, they'll perish while the cricket survives. Rats - they will survive. Dogs will survive because their natural defense is the necessity of their emotional support in a cruel world. If there was one man, one chicken, and one dog left on this planet, the man would feed the chicken to the dog and let himself die of starvation. Man is doomed anyway. We have so many tools to destroy each other and so many electronic tools that we've become reliant on for survival that we couldn't manufacture on our own anymore. The biggest hurdle we have is our gestation period. A human needs massive amounts of care through at least 2 or 3 years of life. Most mammals figure out how to walk on the day they're born, and many have a decent chance of survival after just a week even if they're totally stranded.

Chaos will eventually come in one form or another, and humans are going to have a tough time staying at the top of the food chain. A species' long-term survival is about surviving the ripples of chaos.

Ripples of Tranquility

There is a beauty and art of riding the energy of the ocean. The tide goes out as the moon passes around the horizons east or west, stretching the ocean ever slightly with its gravity. Then when the moon is directly overhead, or underfoot the tide rises back up. This cycle isn't really in rhythm with the sun, so if you lose track you can look at a tide chart to see what's going on up there. The ideal time to get out there is mid tide. The time between high and low. That occurs about twice a day while the sun is still up. So that's when you approach the beach. The waves have a tendency to crash over in the same spots, so you will often see gatherings of surfers at those particular... let's call them wave fields. They are usually just inside the part of the cove where clams gather to do whatever it is they do in their little groups. So once you've determined the proper time, and relative location you can take the next step of charting a course to your waiting point. It's sort of like fishing. You set up and wait for your wave. I like to watch a broad spectrum of beach to find a place where the waves are rolling in, but there aren't too many people. Most people go where the other people are. This is for two reasons. 1, people are idiots and follow their own herd. 2, there is a formation of hard rock that has formed underneath the periphery of the ocean during periods of volcanic activity that created... let's call them berms, although I'm not sure that is the right term. These berms create natural lifts for the current to push the water up against. Now, on the ends of these berms, the waves will push outward. That's where I set up. I ride the sideways waves.

The waves come in sets you know. It's one of the many things you learn from the ocean when you're out there using its infinite energy to move through space-time. Basically, it will be like glass out there, maybe choppy on the surface for about ten minutes. Then you can see a rise move toward you. Then another that might roll over, then another and another. Throughout the sets, the waves form further and further back. So you have to be patient and let a few pass till the one you want comes in. But if you're too patient and the wave now breaks further back then you are, it'll fall right on you and smash you to the crag. If you do get your wave you have to see where it is in its cycle in order to know whether to be forward or back on your board. Too far forward and you're smashed to the crag. Too far back and the wave either passes under you or flips you ass-over-tea-kettle. If you get the wave and are moving forward in a good position, the next step is to stand up. So you do a push-up, hard. You bring your back foot up, then your front. Your back foot has a cord attached to it by the way so that when you fall, the board isn't taken all the way to shore.

So the stand-up process should take about a second ideally, but for beginners, it's more of a 5 to 10-second process as you kneel, balance, step forward with one leg, then maybe get the other foot on the board, lift your hands off the board and stand yourself up. By this point, the wave has fallen over and is now gently rolling foam. Then you balance front, back, left right. After all this, with a bit of luck, you're standing, moving forward for maybe a few seconds. But most of the time you fail and have to swim back out. This will happen in the middle of the sets, so getting back out can be a real challenge for many different reasons. One of the challenges is other people coming at you on their boards. Don't get your teeth knocked out, or suffer a concussion that will most likely cause you to drown. The other thing you will need to learn is how to wipe out. It's very disorienting, and since the cord is attached to your leg you'll be rolled in all directions - first whichever way the wave rolls you, then whichever direction your board is relative to the way you're facing.

The next dynamic to consider is swells. Swells are created hundreds of miles away by storms usually. High or low-pressure pockets create either a rise or a depression over a wide expanse of sea. After a few days that form evens out by arriving at land, beach land. The tides these days are about ten feet, and the waves at mid tide have been about 8 feet. So if your feet were attached to the ground for a few second as a wave was coming in, your head would be just on the surface, then 8 feet under. The current has been slow but I haven't figured out why. So if you got up on a wave 100 feet from shore, you would reach the shore in about 30 seconds. In a faster current that ride might only take 10 seconds.

Ideally, the wind is blowing into the ocean from land. That can basically happen anywhere but is common in only a few regions around the world. One of those places is here in southern Nicaragua just east of the volcano lake island named Ometepe. There are two volcanos on the island. The heat from those volcanos creates a steady wind west to this beach. The reason this offshore wind is important is that it basically holds the wave up as it's coming to shore. If the wind is coming from behind the wave, like on most beaches, the wave falls right over. When the wave is held up you get that famous curl effect. You can ride in the tube. That's basically all you need to know about surfing.

Gerardo drives Tim, Joe, Plum, and myself to the pier of the lake that separates San Juan del Sur from Ometepe. We're going to go check out this wonder of nature. After a heartfelt goodbye, we hop on the ferry and have a pleasant boat ride to the island. When we arrive we meet an interesting creature who calls herself Flo Stow. She's a 19-year-old student from England backpacking Central America by herself. Kids these days?!? Anyway, like every other person from England I've met in foreign countries, she's a riot. We invite her to take a shuttle with us to the other side of the island where we'll be staying for the next couple days. She hops right in, casually fearless. We drive east for around an hour through the skinny part of the island between the two volcanoes and end up at a decent enough hostel.

Probably the best decision I've made in months was to sleep in when my four mates climbed up one of the volcanoes. Fuck that, it's too hot out even at 7 am. I climbed one of these bastards a few years ago. I find it's much more pleasant to observe them from below. As expected they come back exhausted and underwhelmed. We have a few more adventures then call it a chapter. Tim and Plum are headed back to Vail, and Joe and I are going south to Costa Rica to meet up with another friend from Vail.

Flo Stow is hitchhiking north into Honduras. While looking off at the world and sipping our pre-departure cups of coffee, she teaches me how to count birds. *One for sorrow, two for joy, three for girl, four for boy, five for silver, six for gold, seven for a secret that should never be told.* That's basically all you need to know about counting birds.

Costa

"You've made a few cameo appearances in my dreams since I've been down here. It's kinda nice to wake up thinking about you, but a bummer to realize you're not actually in my bed." It's the kind of simple love note that will entice a girl to pack up and leave her parents' house for good. Hopefully... maybe. It's been a year now. I still think of my Lee often obviously, and she tells me the same. For some reason, it's hard for me to believe that a girl may have prospects of making me hers, but I suppose it's very normal, almost inevitable. My Lee is in her mid to late 20's now I believe, and even though I'm about ten years older than her, I think we might be a good match.

She'd cozy up to me so sweetly in our moments in Thailand. And when she came out to visit me in Vail this summer, there was a real magic. There was something powerful. There's a reservation though. I gather that it would be different if I was Jewish. Sounds dumb, but it's true. She admitted it once when I asked in a roundabout way. Also, I'm still not sure how to process her distaste for monogamy, especially considering she lives in Miami - the 2nd porn capital of our debaucherous country behind Los Angeles. In any case, I sent her that brief love note, and we'll see how she responds.

A couple years ago I was here in Costa Rica with a girl I met in a mental institution. We reconnected a few years after our time in the loon bin. She visited me in Vail, we had a real nice weekend and met up again a few months later in Costa. She had stopped taking her meds a month or so earlier, which is fine... until she started getting real angry and aggressive out of nowhere a couple days in a row. One night as we were driving back from town, she threw my dinner out the car window for no reason. I hate to admit it, but manic people are fucking scary sometimes. I left her the next day to fend for herself in Central America. It sounds harsh, but I did the world a favor leaving her behind. She made it back to the states safely, but obviously, we didn't speak anymore after that. I hope she remembers her lesson. I hope everyone has learned their lesson at my expense, and that the world is a slightly better place. Slightly better for me to walk around in. I hope I have learned my lesson of where I should walk.

Joe and I spend the extra dough to take a nice air conditioned bus across the border. The chicken bus was an experience, but I don't need to do it again. Joe's a real meatball. Always a good time. From Chicago, bartender, tells great jokes, loves cocaine, skies leisurely. He's a funny one to travel with. Always has to be lining up a plan, then changing plans, then getting all flustered when we come to a crossroad and I evaluate alternatives. It's funny. It's like it's too much for his head to handle sometimes. In particularly stressful times he pulls up a Cubs game on his phone, watches a few innings and is as good as new in a couple hours. Happy fella. Good mate.

Tamarindo is another surf town on the Pacific, but a little more built up than San Juan. Joe and I get pretty drunk familiarizing ourselves with all the beachfront bars and end up at some rinky-dink casino gambling our money away on video roulette. I wake up in a hammock with a half full beer bottle underneath me. I can tell that this day is going to be a total waste, but I struggle to choke down a breakfast beer to kill the hangover and we head to the beach to ride a couple waves.

I awake with an equation beside my head. It's an 8 x 7 grid diagonaling down to the right with variations in the hatchlings. I'm alone on the beach somewhat rejuvenated after making a mental imprint of the hatch I must have scribbled while exhausted. I decide it's my destiny to stand on my hatch with one foot, grab the other behind my body and point like a yoga man into the direction I'm facing - west by northwest approximately. It's the location where I had collapsed about 20 minutes earlier after getting beaten by the sea. I must have dragged myself out of the sea, and laid down on my back on my surfboard just out of the water. I guess I basically fainted there in the blazing sun with my right arm covering my eyes to shield the sun. I must have chicken scratched my equation with my lifeless dangling left arm. I don't know what it says really, but I hope that the powers that gave it to me noticed that I was a good conduit and that I will await further instruction.

After a few days, Joe heads off to meet up with that other friend of ours from Vail before flying off to Chicago for a wedding. I'll be continuing my adventure up on the Yucatan peninsula. It's a region of Mexico that's shaped like an upside down Florida. I don't know what I'll do there, just kill time until June I guess. I guess I'll scuba dive. Maybe I'll get lucky and be allowed to make love to a beautiful woman. I haven't seen so many hot chicks in one place ever. And the bathing suits here are comical. Girls basically wear belts that have a string attached at the front that goes down their crotch and up in their butt cheeks and reattach to the back end of the belt. They might as well just wear belts... or nothing at all. Their whole butts are out there for everyone to see. It's a gas.

I haven't fallen in love yet I don't think. That Flo Stow girl had potential, but she was scandalously young, even for a hostel hook up. What a hoot though. There was another girl from New Zealand that seemed to be down for whatever, but I was too lazy to make any moves I guess. It's this heat man, it really takes the wind out of my sails (that's what I'm going to tell myself anyway to feel better about being unable to get a piece of pussy here in poon paradise.) Let's see, what else... oh, there were those two birds from Europe that Joe and I met while poaching the pool at their luxury hotel. A German and an Italian who said they were in boarding school and are daughters of ambassadors or something. I believe it. I offered to take their picture with their fancy camera, and to be funny I told them to kiss. The one was going right in for it, but the other sort of gave her a cheek. I'm sure they scissor and diddle each other all the time. I hope they do anyway. But I'm not in love with them. Or maybe I am, and they are in love with me, and we have decided that it wouldn't be appropriate for me to be writing love journals about our passion.

The Fen

It takes me a minute to figure out that I'm sleeping in a ten person dorm. I'm laying here trying to process a very vivid dream: The girl I left behind in Philly when I moved out to Colorado is starting a job at the restaurant where I wait tables. She wears nice business attire like she did back then. She seems like I remember her. Sort of helpless, but trying her best. Everyone around their table is responding to that and helping her get everything just right. I'm in my black and white butler uniform attending to the needs of the guests and cleaning up after them like the servant I am in real life now. I try not to be seen by her. I don't think she knows that I work there yet. I figure she'll find out soon enough though, and may break down and cry like she always used to. We catch eyes as I'm cleaning a table. She's not distraught at all. Somehow I find out that she has two kids. When her oldest kid gives me back my two umbrellas - one big, and one small, I realize that they were the only possessions of mine that she had left; the only thing that she had to remember by. But she doesn't care. She's moved on. The kid also informs me that she has a third kid, an infant, which surprises me because she looks great. She has a whole family. The kid of hers that brought me the umbrella was basically a form of Rich I think.

In the next sequence, I'm on the train that I used to take to my office job in Philly, but it's going up a mountain in the Rockies. I'm trying to return a call to some important person about a job interview that I skipped in order to go to a baseball game. I think Jenna was on the train... Yes, she was the ticket taker.

I wake up not knowing where I am, maybe the hull of a ship... it's another new dream sequence. There's a river of water running past the window of my room on the second floor. I go downstairs and see my wife outside on the back porch seeming sad. She's been working on the computer being productive and doesn't quite believe me when I tell her the river of water that is no longer there was coming up to my window. I apologize for the broken glass on the sliding door to the porch even though I don't think I broke it. It looks like it had been punched. I think we were both sad that we have no kids.

175

God, how I wish it would rain today. I'm still in my dorm bed, haven't moved yet just laying here with my eyes closed. The drapes are drawn shut so it's totally dark in the room, but I hear people moving around in the kitchen. That'll be my next move. I'll go drink coffee, and I guess sit on a porch or in a hammock and watch everyone move about the hostel. For the last couple days, there's been a pack of French speaking people passing through, and I think there is a German couple too. Most of the time people speak in English in very thick accents.

I awaken and move outside, up in a very nice open air loft sitting on a bean bag chair. My ceramic coffee cup is chipped right in the spot where I put my lips to drink while holding the loop in my right hand. I like that for some reason. I suppose I have awoken very calm today.

I believe I have a bit of an interpretation to my dream. I believe that I want children. I basically always have. But as the years go by I think I've grown accustomed to the lifestyle that my wretched personality has afforded me. Independence, freedom, solitude, fortitude. It's not that I need a genetic copy of myself. I'd like offspring as a glue between me and my wife for whom I would love to try my best to nurture.

How great it would be if the impossible happened and I come into a union with a wife that could be tender and supportive in all my victories and failures; understanding that when I'm not really doing anything, it's because I can't; because I'm incapacitated with a mind cloud. And trusting that I'll pull it together again like I always do.

Jenna. Jenna the Fen. If I didn't leave for Colorado 5 years ago we'd probably be miserably married right now. She was just so irrational and emotional, especially behind closed doors. I mean more so than most girls. But my my my, did she have my heart. I think more than anything it was the way we slept. That and something else that I've never exactly been able to put my finger on. She was incapable of lying. It's like she didn't have the confidence, or know it was something a person could do.

I believe she's married now to her very own eggplant husband. She has achieved stability. But now she probably must be struggling every day with the idea of having kids, and the reality of the pain of labor and childbirth, and lifestyle changes. And by struggling, I mean panicking every second. Pressure from family and maybe her husband. She does what the family tells her. It's all she knows. She's very afraid of the outside world. She once told me that she is scared of space - like outer space. That seemed silly to me. It's like being afraid of air. I mean air basically connects right to space, right? How could she not see that? I guess I can see why. I get it. It can be a dizzying prospect to live in the middle of eternity.

I'm not sure what to write about now. I'm just not that into it anymore I think. I could give a journal-like summary of the day. I could go on about my worldly observations and opinions. I could tell you about my mood or interactions I've had recently with the babes out here. It doesn't matter though. I'm only out here right now in order to wait. I'm just waiting for it to be June so that I can move into my new apartment, and go back to work. I have zero to do till then. I tried to think of something productive I could do with this time, but couldn't come up with anything besides save the rainforest or discover a new element.

But I suppose it is my duty to write a log entry for today... The last time I entered my log it was into my sweet darling love Jew Lee from Israel. I don't know if we'll meet again. I think maybe she's too much like the loose women of our time. Too much like myself giving away the secrets of her body to the sex panthers of the region - the outgoing goofs that travel to popular places and make 50 attempts a day at a log entry. And then they scribble all over each other notes that will go unread. Jotting themselves away. Like myself. It's a sad prospect. It's a sad truth. How does a person get on in such a landscape? I suppose ignorance and naivety are a trait I should be looking out for in a woman. And some sort of forgiveness for past transgressions. Although, for some reason, women tend to see a gigolo as some sort of challenge. A prize to be had if she can lock him down maybe. The virtuous ones are not as sought after. It must be for some instinctual reason. Something about dominance of the species.

The transformative cuddle fish will change color in excellent displays of a light show to attract mates; also to hypnotize prey before they pounce. But one of the most effective methods that only some of them possess is to transform into the form of a female and take in the light show with the other gals, then when all the commotion is over and the dudes have left, the imposter reveals his true colors and makes the time with all the lady cuddles. Did you know that dolphins have sex for fun? They do. So I guess it's ok. Condoms. I don't think dolphins wear condoms or use the pull out method, but I could be wrong on that one. They use more of their brain than humans. They possess the power of telepathy. Electro waves of conversation that accompany their chirping sounds. They have a very interesting vocabulary. They often understand over a hundred human commands such as "balance the ball on your nose" or "give me a boost into the air". Humans have been able to decode only a handful of their vocabulary. But that's probably conversation from dolphin to dolphin. We don't know what they're trying to tell us to do. They told me to travel to the beach today. So it is my duty to abide. I will try my hardest to send out an electromagnetic wave into the abyss of the mother ocean. I suppose I'll do it between sets of waves while I am waiting on my surfboard.

Poc-na

With progress comes the slums. It becomes apparent on the bus ride from the Cancun airport to downtown Cancun 20 minutes away that this part of Mexico has its city grid and infrastructure in much better shape than Costa Rica. And Costa Rica has itself put together better than Nicaragua by a mile. In Nicaragua's case, the civil war put them back even though it was 30 years ago. You have to figure 10 years to build out of a war zone, 10 to organize to the point where people could trust the government enough to collectively pay for infrastructure, and then about ten years of growing to cater to the influx of tourist that flock to the beaches. The last ten years have been the real change economically. Currency has dramatically appreciated. A local resident used to be able to get maybe 100 cordobas for a solid week's work. Now you can earn that by selling a coconut to a white chick on spring break. In about 5 years Nica could be where Costa is today. They both still have terribly underdeveloped roads - the main measure of "progress" in my opinion. A population will naturally grow but if the veins of the organism don't grow in proportion, it'll choke. Cancun is Costa Rica 10 years in the future probably. Hotel sector supported by the industrial sector supported by the business and shopping sector all near the transportation hub. It's a newer city planned by groups of people that have learned from humanity's collective experience, and who are each motivated individually by the thirst for the energy commonly referred to as money or wealth. I think it would be impossible for a non-human observer to comprehend this mysterious abstract force that motivates a population to work as a collective, just as it's so difficult for us to truly understand the vehicle that makes a single bacteria, virus, bee, or ant spend their energy working toward their collective's growth. Instinct you might say. Does an infant start with the instinct to acquire wealth? If it learns that wealth is what's needed in order to live and procreate, then yes. I suppose it's just instinct and survival that made you wake up and go to work today.

But no. That doesn't explain the psycho-sexual attraction to art and music for example. I was thinking too much like a male. Love, fear, curiosity... these are even more abstract and get to the heart of what

179

shapes our reality. The female of the species is usually more powerful than the male. She determines value, which in term determines wealth. She feels. She determines if your spirit is worthy to pass on to future generations.

Mexico. I don't know what I'll do here. I hope it doesn't get as hot as Costa. It's been ok on the beach - hot, but with a nice breeze. I definitely prefer the cold. It's refreshing. Crisp cool dry air. That's the best. But Mexico is where I seem to have taken myself this time, so I suppose I need to just roll with it. I have 2 weeks here, and I have 2 different ideas of how I want to spend them. Inland where the Incas and Mayans used to live, or on the coast where octopus populate the sea. I should do some diving for sure. And there is this town called something like Oaxaca or something like that that has been calling my name. "Montgomery" it says to me. "Come to me, child". Maybe I will and maybe I won't, Oaxaca. I do what I want bitch. She gets the picture. They all do eventually.

Lugubrious. I have no idea what that word means, but it is swirling around in my head all morning. A sexy friend of mine from Vail told me that I need to check out Isla Mujeres while I'm here. There's not too much going on in the part of Cancun where my hostel is. It's a good base of operation though, so I book it for another night. I throw a couple items in my small day pack and head out to explore. On my way to the beach, I notice that there's a boat for Isla leaving in just a couple minutes so I might as well check it out. It looked a lot closer on my map then it does from the boat. Oh well, it's nice to be on the water anyway.

My first impression getting off the boat is that this place is dumb. People drive around in golf carts for some reason. On every corner is a place to rent golf carts. I figure I'll have a few beers and burritos on the island, then head back to the mainland. But as I'm on my way back to the dock I stumble on to paradise. Poc-na is a super dank hostel right on the beach - bars, stages, hammocks everywhere, volleyball court, pool table, ping pong, libraries, great restaurant with cheap food, awesome bunk rooms, art painted on the white walls everywhere, all for only 15 bucks a night. Someone must have donated their fortune to subsidize this hippie commune because the tiniest little box of a room everywhere else on the island is out of control expensive. There must be a catch. I'll probably be sacrificed to the half-moon tonight. Whatever, sign me up. And while you're at it, sign me up for some scuba tomorrow. I am having a most lugubrious holiday.

All my stuff is still on the mainland, but I can get by for the night with what I have on me. Christ, I think I can get by for a lifetime with what I have on me. You don't need much here. So I'm double booked for the night, no big deal. I'll have to swing back to the mainland tomorrow to pick up the rest of my stuff, but it's not a problem, all part of the equation.

A kitty cat lays down on my table just as I'm about to begin daydreaming. How preposterous. If all the kitty cats on this island are so preposterous I don't believe I will come back tomorrow. The early evening guitar player seems to have shut up finally. He was playing something jazzy in a mode I recognized but couldn't exactly place. Maybe with some sort of a tri-tone substitution. I believe there's a "party" starting out by the tiki bar closer to the beach. Apparently, it's a nightly occurrence. I'm not really interested, but there's free beer I believe. Hmmm, I just noticed that besides this kitty cat laying in front of me, I am completely surrounded by young sexy women from around the world. No dudes, only chicks. This is weird. Oh, look who it is now. The puppy dog I met earlier today. This place is a zoo man.

If you're wondering if I'm prepared for a tsunami, the answer is yes. I'm about 50 meters from the Atlantic Ocean, about 2 feet above sea level. If anything tectonic were to occur I'd have to act fast. After contemplating a few plans I decide that the best thing to do will be to climb the nearest coconut tree. I think I still remember the skill from when my mates and I used to climb lamp posts in Brixton parking lots.

181

I suppose I should pick out one of these dames for my evening pleasure - perhaps a blonde from Peru, or maybe an Asian. No, she's probably a spy. I can't tell how many spies are here. It must be some sort of trap for someone. Probably not me, but maybe. Am I on tv right now? Check all the channels.

Cat is still here on my table, little dog just pranced by, and Asian spy just sat down at the picnic bench in front of me. She tells me her name is Daisy. A likely story. I should ask her if she would like to go out and bring me back a hamburger and a cup of coffee. Then we'll see who the spy is. A young chap named Anthony overhears us talking about skiing, and tells us about the mountain town he's from. It's a pretty funny story because it's the same mountain town I'm from. Another spy.

Yes, we have a whole host of characters here at Poc-na hostel, Isla Mujeres. I haven't looked up the translation for Poc-na, but Isla Mujeres translates to the island of women. Well ok, The Dude abides. I guess I'll go get a cold beer and do some salsa dancing on the beach.

Tomorrow I will emerge myself under the water and try to release a pulse of supersonic energy into the universe. A pulse of thanks, I suppose, and maybe a plea for forgiveness. No, that's silly and immature. I will emit raw emotions of rage, love, and confusion. That should be enough to break the plane. I will listen for a response and do as I am instructed. That's how I ended up walking north for three days in mid-May 2005. At that time I had stopped taking the pills that the normalcy doctors gave me. They were composed of a mysterious element called lithium. A heavy metal/salt I believe. It dampened the messages I was receiving from the electrodes of the ocean. It was in May 2001 that the electrodes told me to join the nautical navy to be a flyer. I have since abided my calling to follow the seasons to and from the highest point in North America. A land free from moisture where I can receive my orders from whales and aliens without static interference.

I'm almost late for the dive when I get back from Cancun, but I check in, grab some gear and hop on the rig with the rest of the crew. It's been a year since I last dove but I'm pretty sure I remember how to do it. I am mistaken. It takes me 15 minutes to remember that inhaling makes you rise subtly and exhaling makes you sink, so to compensate I keep unnecessarily using up my oxygen to fill my suit with air and releasing it over and over. This is not a great activity to try to relearn on the fly. I'm struggling down here. The guide is losing patience with me and has to come help me adjust my buoyancy several times even after she attached the extra weight to my belt to keep me down. I know I have an oxygen gauge and depth meter, but I can't find them. My mask is filling up with water and I can't quite remember how to clear it. Ok, now I remember, you point your head up and breathe out your nose.

I start thinking through what I'd do in the scenario that my regulator falls out... the regulator is basically the breathing apparatus connected from the tank to your lungs via your mouth. If it falls out of your mouth there's a method for finding it and getting it back in. So I'm trying to remember how to do that, find my gauges, keep track of the group, stay at a steady depth, and breathe. Breathing is not as easy as you might think. It must be done very slowly. The worst thing that can go wrong when you're diving is you start to panic and hyperventilating. I'm still drifting up and down instead of maintaining a steady depth. I finally find my gauge only to realize that I've already used up two-thirds of my air. I can't remember the hand signal to tell this to the guide. I start trying to recall the process for going back up, but I remember that if you do it wrong your lungs explode and your eyes pop out of your head. I'm starting to panic. I send out my electromagnetic energy telegram to the dolphins, and they tell me just to breathe like a yoga man and enjoy their house of tangents.

Eventually, I get to a stable depth of about 50 feet and start going around the sea floor with the rest of the group. Fish everywhere... obviously. It's a different world down here man. Fish treat you like fish. Coral is such a bizarre formation of living rocks. I always talk about how the cities and farm systems that man creates emulate his natural world, but coral is quite a different beast. I'll have to dream on that for a while before I get back to my house. Where is that anyway? Doesn't matter.

We come back to the surface and I have no clue where I am or how I got here. It doesn't feel right to be breathing natural air. I'm panicking again, and I can't talk. I'm floating though, so I guess that's a good thing. I see the boat like the finish line that I need desperately to get to. I sort of cut everyone off and start climbing the ladder and removing equipment in the wrong order, but I just have to get out of the sea and sit down. I don't think I'm visibly in a panic during any of this time. Nobody really knows I'm struggling and I still don't have the power of speech to be able to tell them. I recognize that I'm on the boat but I'm totally disoriented. I can't see two feet past my face. I feel like I'm still under water and can't stop breathing like a yoga man; probably because I haven't heard the dolphin tell me to stop.

So I'm just sort of existing on short slow breaths. I feel like I'm thinking about breathing but not actually breathing. I start to look around. I'm totally lost. I remember learning about this condition in one of my classes in Thailand. I think it's called nitrogen poisoning. Nitrogen is an inert gas, and when you dive it builds up in your body and just sort of hangs out. I forget how it happens or why it screws your brain up so much, but nitrogen poisoning is a somewhat common occurrence in diving, and it feels like a cross between tripping on acid and doing nitrous balloons. I deal with it like the Navy man that I am. Adapt and overcome. Relax. Do the next thing. A person is talking to me. Look at them, try to regain focus. This is where a history of getting high on drugs comes in handy. Knowing how to recognize that even though your face is melting off, everything is fine and you just have to push through. Everyone is back on the boat now and I've regained my powers of speech enough to tell one of the guides what's going on. He tells me to eat an orange and relax. Great advice mate. Everyone's eating oranges for some reason. I guess it's snack time.

The second dive is coming up and I tell the guide that I'm just going to stay in the boat. He tells me that the best thing I can do to recover my senses is to get back under water. Ok. Down we go. He's right. I feel totally normal again down here. This time I can enjoy the entire dive. I've remembered all the dynamics and equipment operation. We swim up to a set of sculptures that had been placed down here for coral to grow on. There's a leatherback sea turtle hanging out by a statue of a man. I think I remember having a dream of this moment once - like a dream deja vu. Back at the hostel I feel like I'm somewhere between the sea and the surface. I'm exhausted. I take a 4-hour nap to dream the dolphins a message of thanks for saving my ass down there earlier.

My Lee has replied to the message I sent her a few days ago with the same expression of love read just between the lines. She's quitting her job this week and traveling for a while. Makes sense. Why not. If I were her I'd do that with the loose intention of moving to Vail, to pick back up with the career and lover that she knows are both waiting there for her. It's a fairy tale custom woven for a Jewish princess. When she visited me this past winter, I partially felt like I was selling her on the idea of moving to Vail. Everything fell into place. The people we met, the random events we attended in casual fashion. It was nice that the weather cooperated too. It was very warm that weekend even though the ski season was in full swing. It gave validity to my claim that there is a misconception of the harshness of the winters in Vail. If I was her, I'd be sold. So anyway, we're making some loose plans to road trip around Colorado and Utah this summer.

I'm already attaching to her all sorts of traits and virtues that only exist in my imagination as I picture our fairy tale future. I'm sure I'm looking past all sorts of character flaws, and things I know nothing about. But she is a darling lass. I really think that she and I could have something great, something that we're both looking for that is clearly right in front of us. How many girls have I said that about? I estimate 30. There have been only a few that I recognized immediately for what they were - passing pleasures. For the most part, my mind just has this way of looking light years past the blink of an eye.

Most of the time I consider myself average at best when it comes to my appeal, but sometimes rays of light fall on my self-perception and I think to myself that I have all the makings of a super gent. Foreign profile, piercing blue eyes, the wit and attention of a renaissance conversationalist. A chauvinist feminist, poet of finance, eternally sophomoric. Silly beyond reason, troubled beyond doubt, lost and forgotten. The motivation of an eggplant and chiseled physique of a sunflower stalk. What's not to love?

French Girls

I'm lying in my fiesta hammock around the break of dusk when the Holy Spirit offers me one wish. I think right past all the silly things like money, love, happiness, and the welfare of all the poor children in the world. Then I remember my original life goal: to walk on the moon. Just as I'm in the process of wishing for that, several young sexy women with loose morals walk up to tell me how much they love watching my gangly arms hang off the sides of the hammock as I swing.

I feel like maybe, just maybe, I could finally be turning things around. I think maybe the Holy Spirit has gotten into my bones, and might just have a chance to live in the marrow of my soul today. I sure hope so. I've just felt like a sinner for so long now. I've had a heart of stone and mud for as long as I can remember.

I haven't been able to spread any kind of joy into the world for decades now. I always appreciate it when it comes my way, and I'm jealous of people that have the ability to take life's difficulties with grace. I've been lucky not to have had too many difficulties in my life for quite a while. Maybe this invasion of the Holy Spirit into my body and mind is a sign. I've been basically sober for the last week. The Holy Spirit may have taken away my alcoholism. Just like that I no longer have any desire to drink booze of any kind.

I've fallen in with a new set of random friends from the hostel. We mostly bum around the island on golf carts and lay in the sun. They're French Canadian girls, so they speak of the acts of love with the casual confident authority that was born into them. They're 25 and 32 years old. The 25 is very interesting with what seems to be a good heart, an intelligent brain, and a patience and serenity that I have rarely seen. The 32 is clearly a mess just under the surface. Such a sad case. One minute she's talking about how she wants kids, and about the man back home that has recently broken her heart, but who is currently writing her love letters. I think to myself, well that should work out just fine for her eventually. Then she tells us she's sad because the guy at the hostel that she's been sleeping with for the last three nights didn't join her for sunset a few hours ago as she thought he would. She blames it on a language barrier. She said she's going to miss him because he is a good and gentle man. Then she starts talking about the guy she was sleeping with less than 24 hours before that guy. So that's basically four people in a state of confusion. A state they'll all have to deal with for the foreseeable future or until they get themselves into another entanglement of emotion. I didn't really think of myself too much in all this, except for my recent sudden vow of devotion to the Holy Spirit that may finally guide me to true happiness, or else an existence of total solitude. Either way is fine I guess.

It's that part of the trip when I pretty much start every day totally disoriented. Where am I? Who am I with these days? How much longer till I go home? Shoot, where do I live? I fake a sense of awareness pretty well though. I'm thinking most people won't ever even know I have Alzheimer's when I'm an old man. Like now, when people talk to me, I understand that they may or may not know me, and that I may or not know them, but I'll always basically go along like we do no matter who they are.

The crux. There's always a point when things become difficult. "Crux" is a rock climbing term that basically signifies the part of the climb that is the most difficult. It defines the climb. Getting to it is usually manageable, but getting past it is the challenge. In Thailand, my crux came early with the Kiwi and the heat stroke. In Italy, the crux was basically hitchhiking a ride to Lecce while having to take a dump so fierce I nearly shit myself. There was a crux of grade school, high school, college, California, the Navy, the nut houses, and solitary confinement in Roanoke City Jail - the defining crux of cruxes.

My Crux in Central America comes as I'm riding a scooter in busy stop and go traffic with a person on the back of my bike that I have only met a couple hours ago. Halfway across the island, a storm rolls in as I'm going as fast as the bike can go to keep up with traffic. I recognize it as the crux and know I just have to get through this. The fun and games get put on hold when the crux approaches. These trips are a great way to hone survival skills. It's all fun and games... and mind expansion... and honing. That's why I do it. Did I survive to tell the tale? Find out in the thrilling conclusion at the end of this sentence.

I listen to a lot of electronica now because I'm in Mexico with children of the future; young sexy people that were born as I was finishing high school. They listen to strange computer noises all day apparently. They've been my only companions for the last two weeks since my mates left. This is the future. I'm quite overwhelmed with the abundance of half-naked sex hounds eager to get wild. I'm frozen with confusion.

I bet most girls in the circumstance of being attractive and living by the beach have had a collective total of 50 men all up inside their collective businesses. Some may have had a total of 300, but they probably come from dysfunctional families where the dad was a fit handsome gentleman in the United States military, and the mom was a cocktail waitress or a hairdresser in a coastal town. I think towns on the ocean produce rabid bunnies - humans I mean, that have a lot of sexual contact with many anonymous partners with little regard for any significance of the act. It's because they're all wearing underwear in public. Their erogenous zones are totally out on display. I've seen several nips and vag holes fall out of their garments at the beach this week. In fact, I've been to several beaches on this trip where girls just don't even wear tops - tits out, if you will. If you're on the beach and introduce yourself to a new person of the opposite sex and shake hands... well, you're touching skin and almost totally naked. That's practically sexual intercourse; especially if you have a raging boner.

My darling Lee lives in Miami. She's in her mid 20's and has been going out to clubs and things like that with a fake ID since she was 17. I have to assume she has had relations with African American gentleman of stunning physical prowess and astronomical sexual conquests. I wonder if I'll see Lee on a pornographic internet video someday. She has two younger sisters in their early to mid teens. When she visited

189

me this spring we were talking about porn and the age people start looking at it. I think I sprung a new thought in her head when I said that her sisters have probably seen all sorts. I mean, it's true. It's psycho-sexual scientific fact. Am I being crass? I'm just talking about statistics and socio-sexual developmental patterns.

I spend another day with the French girls. I step out for a stroll and a bite to eat with the 25. She tells me about her recent heartbreak. It was a strange one and just another reminder that I cannot exist in this world of madness. Girls are fucking morons when it comes to love. She's a nice girl though I guess. I think she is anyway, but actually, I have a feeling that beneath the surface is pure hell. She seems to take pleasure in many of the same comforts of affection as I do, but as she tells me the story of how the guy she longs for was cheating on her with another dude, it's obvious that she cannot help but be attracted to the same train wrecks as all the rest of the pretty girls, French or otherwise.

Both of the French girls talk about how certain things make them "sad". Sad is a word people don't really throw around in my normal life. "I was sad", they would say in their foreign voices slightly deeper than most girls. They say things like - it will make me sad when he is gone, or, I was sad and it will make me cry. It's just interesting to hear people talk openly about an emotion that I think most people are embarrassed to admit. I don't know what it is about that word that has caught my attention over the last couple days.

This place is a hippie commune. There are a few babes coozing with desire around a drum circle of fools. It reminds me of a girl I met this past ski season. I was cautiously interested and I suppose so was she. But she changed her tune and told me about her plans to go to South America to be with this "tam-tam" player that she has fallen for even though she knows it's a ridiculous prospect. What the fuck is a tam-tam and what is it about this guy that makes a girl desire him so bad to travel to the other side of the world for him while I'm sitting right next to her on the chair lift? The indifference of these women further breaks my spirit and diminishes my hope for the possibility of a partner that hasn't been tricked by the distractions of the world, and tainted past the point of no return by all its evils.

Why do I spend my life in these vacation destinations where studs flock to the women displaying their sexy bodies half naked competing for the lay of the alpha meat head, or the next peacock with a silly man-bun. There's one now seducing the beautiful girl under the shade tree. So young. She seems like she's trying to figure out how this scene works, and what she's supposed to do. Look at their tattoos and spectacular suntans, she thinks. She has the innocent face of a Greek statue. She looks confused and stunned, and she walks off with her head down. She returns with the determination to satiate the curiosity that this loony tune has inspired. They'll be heavy petting by sundown. She never even had a chance. Oh well, I guess that's the natural progression toward womanhood that I've been watching from the sidelines all these years. What is a girl in her tweens doing here... what the hell am I doing here? Oh Christ, now man-bun is off with the next batch of chicks dazzling them with his group selfies. If porn has taught me anything it's that girls will do anything to have their picture taken.

The gals will go back to tell the naughty tales of their debauchery around the sewing circle while the other side of the sexual conquests competes for who got the most pussy for the trip. Fast forward ten years and these mothers, fathers, sons, and daughters are trying to recreate this artificial passion that has watered down their reality.

Maybe I need to approach this scene like the dazzling cuddle fish. Lose to win. Let the alphas battle it out and take their spoils, and find a perspective from the inside as one of the French gals. No, that's basically being a gay homo. Although I know some that switch teams regularly and take a few prize pieces. But no, that's not my game, that's not my race.

One of the Poc-Na hippies told me that an octopus can change its DNA if it needs to. Maybe I should try to learn how to do that. Chicks go bananas for shapeshifters. Humans, even tribal primates, can craft metal into triangles to swing as weapons, strap to feet as snow claws, or fasten together microscopically and modularly as computer chips. That sort of ingenuity always seems to get the ladies going. But I'm too old to learn any of those tricks.

I'm looking for someone who's turned off by this charade. Not just turned off, but actually intelligent enough to not get distracted and taken by the very thing they claim to despise. The fact that I'm here I guess proves the point that I wouldn't meet my stupid criteria either. I'm as bad as the rest. One day I'll find my way out of this mess.

So where do I look for this candle that's glowing? In a cave maybe. This world makes me sad... No, enough self-pity, Shawn. I'm looking at this all wrong. There must be plenty of gems hiding in plain sight just like myself. Where would these diamonds be patiently sharpening their souls? Running from the sun maybe, out on Highway 61. That's where I'll find her - striding in front of me at the speed of fate. If I put my mind to it I should be able to catch up to her eventually.

What happened?

I look up from my tiki bar lounge chair and see two planes racing overhead. But no, it is an illusion. They are stars, and it's the clouds that are rapidly moving past. They are moving away from the Atlantic Ocean which is two blocks away from the rooftop bar I'm sitting at. So that means they're moving rapidly west and I think - hmmm that's queer, there must be some sort of low-pressure traffic jam inland on the Yucatan. Then I realize that I'm in a tropical zone, Cancer or Capricorn, I forget which, but weather moves east to west here, so everything's fine. All systems seem to be normal, weather and otherwise.

Sliding sideways into the end of the trip. It's getting too hot for me here. My back hurts from carrying my pack all around. I opt for a private room with air-con in a roadside motel instead of another hostel. I guess I'm tired of meeting the same kinds of travelers. They call them youth hostels for a reason. Young people wander to these places, and somehow these collectives form. I enjoy the spirit of these places, but after a month I'm ready to be an adult again.

But this compromise isn't great either. I've spent more time in my room than out for the last couple days. It's ok though. Rest is a necessity. In the upside of my down time, I explore some Mayan ruins of Tulum and Coba. To relax from my slumber I swim in the cool water at the openings of these strange naturally formed underground aqua-tunnels called cenotes.

Instead of the buzz of beachgoers in the streets and the smell of sea air, I'm smelling the dust kicked up from the trucks shooting across this highway type road. I'm eating salty eggs and pretending to enjoy the instant coffee that George the cook has given me. He's short with a squeaky voice and does a pretty good job trying to speak English. He laughs and argues with the other girl behind the counter; maybe his wife or something like that. My guess is that she loves him, but he doesn't care.

He talks a good game. He wears a Bulls cap and says he likes Michael

193

Jordan. I don't really trust him though. People like him try to take advantage of people like me all the time out here. For longevity, it's best to be nice, but keep your guard up with people like George. Usually, they're good people, but the roadside truck stop near tourist sites anywhere in the world can have charm and appeal. So do spider webs to the bee. You can't hate the spider for finding a nice corner to set up in, and you can't blame the ant for tiptoeing past. Don't hate the player, hate the game if you want. But in the end, you get what you pay for. Be wise about where you spend the spoils of the traps that you and your brood have laid.

I just wonder what's going to happen next. I feel like nothing has happened in a long time. I remember there were a few babies that got born. People were all upset about this gorilla at the zoo that got shot, but that's barely anything. Everyone loves the Bernie Sanders show, but then there's the Trump train right behind it. So that's something maybe, but no, that's all a distraction too... just news really. What's happening? Weather is always happening. That's pretty cool I guess. I have no idea. I think my mom said she saw the rings of Saturn through Joe's telescope last week. She said he ran in through the back door all in a tizzy about it. She didn't say tizzy though. I'm embellishing. I wonder if Rich looked at the rings of Saturn through Joe's telescope too. That's not nothing either way. He just graduated college two days ago. Joe I mean. The last I heard Rich is still in college, but only for one or two more decades I think. I guess Joe will be moving back to Brixton to be roommates with mom and Rich. I assume he'll get a job at the big-pharma farm and pick up with the research that his father was working on; boner pills maybe, or opioids, or pretend cures for cancer.

I'm sorry, but as it turns out there is nothing happening. I doubt anything will happen tomorrow either. Christ, what was the last thing that even happened? I just can't remember. I must have died and gone to purgatory. That's not so bad I guess. It's not great, but it could be worse.

A long time ago, my imaginary friend told me I make things too complicated. She told me I'm building my life's pyramid from the top down. She was right. I was just following the instructions though. I started with a sturdy foundation and worked toward a single point just as the blueprints indicated, but since I started from the sky and worked my way to the ground the end result was a pyramid with its head in the sand, balancing upside down, teetering, tempting gravity and the elements to knock it over.

I've simplified since then. I still build from the sky down, but now I start with the tip and work down to the base. I'm very pleased with the results of my normal looking pyramid. It's simple. Sit on a plane, drink a beer, set up in a cheap hostel, go to a beach or monument, drink more beer, maybe have a love affair, take pictures, write a parable, take an exhausting journey home, go back to work for a season, donate to charity, paint your car, fix your bird, mix soup, consume blindness, build a pyramid from the sky down, go to bed and have a dream.

6

Gradually then Suddenly

Fractal Silhouette

a universe stuck in the habit of being fractal; where nothing ever actually touches anything else. Near, far, it's all the same. Everything is effected by everything else's gravity, but ultimately infinity singular. An infinite amount of singularities, or one single entity bound by souls and feelings.

I just don't have the energy right now. I'm running low on energy. I'll need more energy. I think the elevation has gotten to me. Yes, that's exactly what it is. My body is adjusting to the altitude. I've never gone directly from sea level back to Vail at 8200 feet.

Maybe I should have let my body adjust for a couple days before heading another 3000 feet into the atmosphere for this camping trip. Christ, half of my worldly possessions are still jammed in my truck since I haven't yet taken the time to unpack them into my new apartment - a tiny studio on the back side of Vail.

We find a place to set up our tents just at the tree line - the line where trees somehow instinctually come to a unanimous decision that beyond this exact elevation they will refuse to attempt growth. Typically this is right around 12,500 above sea level.

Clark the Shark pulls up just after the sun goes down. As per standard, he has brought a metric fuck ton of naturally occurring organic compounds that will be illuminating the mind eye of the collective. His lover with the multicolored eyes and two other chaps step out of the car... you've got to be kidding me... is that Anthony from Poc-na. I guess it makes sense since he and Clarky work together, but come on... I just met this guy two weeks ago in Mexico. This town is ridiculous. While those two get to work building a second fire and filling the forest with trap tunes, Jessi girl and her beau are confusing each other about loony tunes, Linz is looking for the food, the crew dudes are fetching fire fuel, and I'm in the kitchen with the tombstone blues. Whew.

Our existence as a species on this planet seems to be moving right along. I haven't thought too far past the point of rebuilding humanity, but that's mostly because it's just too early to tell how it's gonna shake out at this point. That's fine. Everything is fine and going along the natural freeze/thaw process of nature.

Everyone can spin their wheels in this woman's world, and the studs can take a back seat to the alpha ding dong for a while, but it will be very easy to tell when the rest period is over, and it's time to accept that the farm villages are burnt, the only food is grass and fresh kill, and every day you have to decide if you stay behind to salvage the fallen, or press on toward higher ground, fresh water, and a safe haven. There are no wrong answers... especially when people stop counting their crows and squabbling over the most efficient conveyor belt.

I look up at space through a grove of trees that Clark is floating around in, and I see a fractal path being taken from our world to the next. A pine tree. It's not growing. It's not leaning or moving up. It's going forward as I observe it from my simple perspective of a man going forward in time. It's projecting itself like I project myself. It's frozen though. It's not even really here as far as it knows - because it doesn't know time.

Look up at a big sky of stars from the base of a groove of ponderosa pine trees and change your perspective to comprehend up as forward. The Great Tree has an eye at the tip top. It looks forward forever. As the earth spins, it scans in slow motion as it drops pine cones, dies, and sprouts up again right next to itself in a new fractal pattern. From that perspective, the trees are sort of time machines... more like bridges to a time-space conduit that we don't exactly see. But we do. We look past it though for the sake of... reason. And that's fine. Everything is just fine. Opinions on any of this or that are a just another discovery of alternate perspectives.

Our collective ingenuity is flawed at this point though. We can't seem to figure out prime numbers. The conclusion of theoretical physics is that there are an infinite amount of parallel universes. The laws of astrophysics and quantum physics break down at right about the size of space that we live in. And none of this really jives with the more tangible metaphysical realm we live, breathe, and love.

As far as our species' collective conscience can tell, there is almost an infinite amount of open empty space... I'm not really taking about space outside our planet, but inside our bodies. An atom is 99.999% empty space between the nucleus and the orbiting electrons. Then you look over to the next orbiting electrons and into their nucleus. Combined with rest it assembles the pyramid of what we react to in our daily lives. Somehow, there we are, floating, sitting on top of it all, willing this collection of stardust along a course we set through this finite clip of infinity. Non-duality, never heard of it. But it's a thing, an idea. God is a thing too I guess and he lives next door to the last prime number.

I have achieved the Great American Dream! I now have a waterfall to look at and listen to from the front porch of my new studio apartment. I'm settled back on the planet earth Colorado. The air here, the air - you just wouldn't believe how clean and crisp the air is here. It's as important as clean water is to fish - literally. I think it is overlooked as a delicacy because it's free, but high rocky mountain air is like a fine bottle of wine. Except it's free.

So I'm breathing my good air again; appreciating it again. The month of travel has stripped away my worries of the details. It's funny how that works. I don't have a bed, a washer/dryer, tv, or the internet. For some reason, my computer no longer plays DVDs or the video games I was into. My entire apartment is one medium sized room. It's a fort. I live in a clubhouse under the waterfall, and that's all. I have a chair, a stove, and a toilet, and that's just great.

And I have a job if you can believe that. I like to work. Hopefully I don't get promoted, but unfortunately, the ranks of middle management have been quitting and getting fired more lately. I'm worried that they might try to pull me up the ladder to fill the void. I like moving chairs, passing appetizers, then going home. I don't like to think about anything. Ever. And I don't want to try to tell someone like me what to do and have to deal with them not doing it right or giving me attitude. I can't survive in the middle. Top or bottom is fine, but anywhere in the middle is no good. Guests can complain to my boss about the details of their event. I'm just at the bottom. It's like my boss works for me as the person that deals with everything while I'm moving chairs and tables, and serving drinks to newlyweds and their kin.

My lovely love Lee informs me that she has quit her job and is roaming free. So, I suppose we'll meet up here soon enough. I'm 100% positive that if I was Jewish we'd be betrothed. Luckily I am not, and we can proceed with our love affair unabated by social norms. She wants me to take her to India. No way. That's literally the last place on earth I'd want to go. They all stand too close to you and smell terrible and have no sense of humor or athletic ability. A nation of one uppers always trying to be better than you. My new year's resolution was to be more open minded toward Indians and Republicans, but I gave that resolution up for Lent and forget about it when Easter came around. Sorry.

I don't get what her attraction is to India. I think it's because a bunch of her backpacker friends has gone there. But she knows it's not a safe place for women, especially when traveling solo like she was when we met in Thailand. I'm trying to convince her that Australia or South Africa would be a better experience. I want to take her to one of those places this fall. Timing is a bit of a problem though. Summer is my season to make most of the money I need for the rest of the year. If she would have cut loose three or four months from now, we'd go on a wild romp around the globe. We'll manage some sort of compromise I hope.

We're talking though. She calls me and writes me that she is thinking of me. And I her, I tell her. She has nothing to gain or lose by trying to be with me, no more than I. Just the love of a true companion. That's not nothing.

I'm half-assing it today. I'm walking around in the woods as if I was behind my neighbor's house scratching around the vicinity looking around for birds or flowers or whatever comes into my realm. I'm dressed like I'm going to church - jeans and a collared shirt that I used to wear to the office in my corporate days. I just felt like putting on this morning. I probably look like a drunkard lost in the middle of a round of golf - so out of place. I stick out like a boner in sweatpants, as the saying goes.

Look at these two lovebirds coming down the trail. People hike with a mission up in these Rockies. He's wearing camouflage pants and his girl has on yoga leggings. They're probably finishing up the ten-mile loop up to Booth Falls. I'm basically trail blazing at what must appear to be a peculiar distance from the trail - maybe twenty yards off the beaten path, just about a half-mile from the parking area. They must think I'm a complete lunatic wandering around. Oh shoot, I know that guy. I used to work with him at the pizza shop. Hello. I don't care. It's funny. It's a hoot. I love a good hoot. More than anything in this world I think what I most love is a good honest hoot.

It's alright

My Lee has flown to Providence. I think that's in Rhode Island, but I might be making that up. Yes, she quit her job, went to Providence, then some bloke asked her to drive his car from California to the east coast. Guess who she wants to meet in Colorado along the way.

It's me. The answer is me.

Shit, I don't even have a bed in my place yet. I'll need to get cracking on that. I'm finally back to work this week after a month off, but I guess I'll have to ask for another few days off to spend with my gal. I should also probably trim my pubes down a little bit.

She tells me she's bringing a friend - her best friend Lynn from childhood. She's also Jewish obviously. I'm happy to be meeting someone so close to her, but this presents a logistical challenge in that I'm a little old-fashioned when it comes to lovemaking. I'm so big on having nonparticipants in the room during the act, and I'm also not too sure how I feel about dicking around in multiple women at the same time. I guess we'll cross that bridge when we come to it. Maybe I can pawn her off on a friend that wouldn't mind keeping occupied for a night or two.

I meet them at the same bus terminal that my Lee got dropped off at when she visited me this past spring. They're a mischievous pair. Lynn's nice though - smart, witty, chill. These girls have come up in very wealthy households, and are underwhelmed back at my place. I threw a couple pictures up on the wall and organized my belongings, but my flat screen TV sits on the floor because I haven't yet bought a stand to attach it to. I still have no cable anyway, so it doesn't really matter. All the fun to be had in this town is outside anyway.

There are pretty legit free concerts in Vail every week in the summers to attract tourists, but usually, half the crowd is locals tripping on acid. So we get all tuned up and check that out. Ziggy Marley is playing - he's one of the late Bob Marley's 500 children. It's a fun show. He sings that banana song I really like. Well, it's not really about a banana at all unless you change the words a little... I guess you had to be there... never mind.

The girls are having a great time, but I still haven't really been able to get me Lee alone, other than for a few kisses on the sly. This Lynn girl is proving to be more of a cock block that Kay was in Thailand. I thought my buddy Todd was gonna take her home tonight, but he dipped out early and now I'm stuck with her again. I think Lynn's feeling awkward about the situation too, and she goes back to my place while Lee and I stay out for a while.

We're coming home on the 1 am bus, and some punk ass little bitch piece of shit starts hitting on my girl. I thought she'd be turned off by this drunk sleaze ball, but for whatever reason, she's fully engaged in conversation. We get off at my stop, and he gets up with us...her. I ask him what his deal is, where he's staying, and he says his house is two more stops up the road.

She's giggling with him and tells me to come along to his place, it'll be fun. Fuck that. I walk up the stairs to my place figuring she'll cut this loser loose and come back with me. But she goes off with him instead. We have come to a fork in the road Lee, and you have walked off with the spoon. And that made all the difference.

I hate this. Fuck. One more nail in the coffin of my ability to love anything in this world. And then this is the part where Justice Mongomery unravels. I don't know who that fucktard is, but I hate him. And since all I saw was his shoes, and I believe red hair... Approximately 195 pounds, 6'2" ish, well, I hate everyone fitting any part of his description and anyone that associates or fucks a person like that. So everyone. Everyone sucks.

I walk in my apartment door and Lynn is asleep on the sofa. I tell her what just happened and am obviously frustrated, but basically indifferent as my faith in humanity has been abruptly extinguished. I shut off my brain and shut my eyes and lay curled up lifeless on the side of my bed facing the wall. I hear Lee come in an hour later but I don't move. I've made up my mind that it's over and that it's pointless to pursue anything further with this girl. I should have recognized that months ago. I'm such a fool.

I can't sleep, so I get out of bed at the first rays of the new rising sun. I walk right out the house and bike into town. She's still there sleeping off whatever cum that idiot pumped into her asshole, and I'm having a cup of coffee.

Riding my bike back 3 miles to my house through wonderful trails of mountainous waterfalls and river streams I decide that my only respectable play here is to kick her out. The train she's taking out to California doesn't leave till tomorrow, but she's a big girl. I'm sure she can find something to do till then... and with the rest of her life. Ha, she has no job. She's drifting, and some dude last week convinced her to pick up his car in California and drive it to Maine. Perfect. She gets a road trip, he gets his car back (and probably a blowjob), and once again I'm a stepping stone along the path of her journey of sexual self-discovery. Great. Everybody wins.

The pathetic thing is that I'm sure she didn't go back to that dude's house and bang him and all his roommates last night. She explains that she's traveling, and just going with the flow. I tell her to listen to herself, and hear what she's saying. I say, look, that's just your thing I guess. You go back with randoms late at night after partying and do whatever. No problem. I just think that's kind of trashy, and I'm not interested. No big deal, but I'd like you to leave.

Lynn has already left without saying goodbye. How rude of her. Lee tries to talk to me, but I tell her I barely slept at all last night, and I want to get a little rest before work. She tries to talk to me again, but I shut it down. How rude of me. My mind is made up and I say, don't you have shit to do to figure your trip out?... The intown bus comes in like 20 minutes. So she packs up her bag and heads out. A few minutes later, recognizing the significance of the moment, I walk out for our sad goodbye. It was nice. It was fine. Maybe, just maybe we'll do it again sometime. But probably not.

I say, see ya later alligator. She replies, after a while crocodile. I wipe the tears from her eyes and... No, that didn't happen. I wish it did though. She says that she wasn't trying to hurt me, but that I intentionally hurt her with my words this morning. I apologize for that and blame it on the strong feelings for her that I have been holding on to for so long. She cries a little. Just tears rolling down her check, nothing dramatic.

I must have looked like the saddest person in the entire world walking away across the parking lot there. Sometimes I don't even try to hide the way I feel even if it's pathetic enough to make a passerby stop what they're doing and stare.

Back upstairs from my porch, I can see her waiting at the bus stop. She's standing out there with her suitcase, and her hair all disheveled in a bun on her head, in her funny shoes, with all her little earrings and finger rings glistening in the morning sun. I hadn't had a girl cry for me in a while. I'd never ever try to do that, but something about it is nice when it's for real. There is something profound about true human emotions when they are shared honestly.

Later in the day, I message her a song to listen to on her ride out of Colorado. It's the best I could come up with for a bittersweet expression of acceptance of feelings that are no more than memories now. Don't Think Twice, It's Alright. I picture her crying a little like I did this morning while listening to it. I had the luxury of a private room though. Head in hand, staying on the end of my breath, I could bleed out the feeling of loss. If she decides to listen to it she'll be going from one bus to another bus, to a train to California.

I think she's a little nervous about the drive. She'll be on her own. I think she's planning on sleeping in the back instead of camping or getting motels. That's probably what I'd do too. In fact, I have done that plenty of times. She'll be driving a Tahoe just like mine. It's a very comfortable vehicle for that. She was going to stop in Vail again on her way back east, but I guess she'll have to figure a different route now. I think her first stop was going to be Vegas. Maybe she'll fuck some dude she meets along life's twisted highway, just like we did back in paradise last year. I'm not upset or bitter or mad at her in any way. I hope she's not either. Have fun girl, be safe.

I hate this. I don't care though. It's getting so routine to be disappointed with everything and everyone for all the same reasons for so long. I'm not really offended or hurt by it too much anymore. I'm not sure if that's a good thing. I'm getting even more cold and distant, and less able to feel human emotions. I think about trying to change something, but even if I could figure out what to change I doubt it's really even worth the effort at this point. I'll just keep getting fired from jobs and relationships, and keep landing in new ones whenever. I shouldn't be sad because this life was already sad, so what's there to even be sad about, sadness? Well, yes. That's the worst. Sadness is a sad thing.

Forgiveness is a good thing though probably. I forgive too often and too easily. That's my problem. I need to learn how to hold so many grudges that negativity just exudes out of my pores. Just kidding. All I do is hold grudges. I should let go of one grudge per day, and maybe at the end of the year, I won't be emitting blackness anymore. I'll try to dedicate time tomorrow to picking a grudge to eradicate.

Not that it's gonna matter for anything. It's like I sort of give up but I don't. Like everyone else finished the race, I still have two laps to go, and they already gave out all the loser trophies. It's not death to give up. It's just a rational step toward maybe starting something else - like sitting down and reading a newspaper.

Coloring book

This mess has me pretty bummed out. I'm kind of shell-shocked at work, and into the next day. I have two long stressful shifts; which is fine because it helps me get my mind off Lee and it keeps me from trying to contact her with an outpour of sorrow.

I have a new problem to worry about now, negative criticism at work. Apparently, it is a popular opinion that I'm sort of lazy at times. Ok, sort of, in a way... but no, not at all. I'm a hard worker with that kind of stuff - lug and tug work. I like it. So when I'm criticized I can't really try harder. The worst part is that now I have to work around people that have that opinion and dish on me behind my back. That makes me self-conscious and unconfident, and leads to mistakes on my end. In my twelve hour shift, I end up missing one simple task and there is holy hell to pay for it. Out of a hundred and ninety-nine tasks I miss one. So today was a loss. I can't deal with this lack of respect - from women, from bosses, from fucking everyone.

I can feel myself sliding off the next cliff. It's been a while, but I recognize the feeling and the movement of the universe. Hopefully, everything works out. Not that it matters. I'll keep going, but it's pretty apparent that I'm coming unwound again.

I'm having a thought that maybe in a person's mind and cosmic destiny there is a light source in the ethos. A beacon that calls them to the surface of the reality that they may one day reproduce children. I feel like I sound like a sick bastard talking about that, but it's the most common thing in the world. Strangers meet, then they come together in some sort of game of souls, then there is a creation of a new miracle. I guess from another perspective it's just a mundane perverted ritual, but I don't know. The ladies know I think. They typically can't lift as much, move as fast, do math or explore complex regions of the earth as well, but they sure see something that I as a lowly male I never will. It's weird to know that. Humbling. But there's this undeniable human thing about age that differentiates our species' genders. You know what they say - wombs become barren, but testicles are forever. Do they say that? I'm sure somebody did at one point or another. But that's not important. What's important is that I tend to fully trust and appreciate a woman's instinct, but then completely abandon it when their piercing gaze of anger comes my way. That's ok, it's just passion.

I get a message from Bro Joe all in a panic about needing to move out of mom's house. He only got done with college two weeks ago and now it sounds like he's dealing with the crushing reality that he needs to make it on his own in this life. It'll be tricky giving him advice on moving out. He hasn't lived there since about the time I got banished. I wonder what the hell is going on in that house. Maybe it's a spooooookkkyyyy house, haunted by the ghost of the Knight Commander of the Equestrian.

I text him a short speck of an idea about his situation, but promise to give him a phone call tomorrow to talk it through. I think the key to getting started after college is to put yourself in a position to catch an opportunity. It's the opening moves of a chess game. I lost about half my pieces in my opening navy/nut house moves and had to start over. That's ok too though. It's the king's gambit.

Your business/science degree is probably somewhat flexible as far as the types of companies that would hire you. So, that means you can pretty much pick a city and move there. So if it was me, all cities being equal I'd move where my friends are, or to a city that interests me. Step two is getting your first dumb job. You'll need some money to pay some bills and a move in the direction of that real job. You'll probably have about 5 dumb jobs before you settle into something good. So the trick is figuring a direction into the unknown. Stay flexible.

It's crazy how quick people get trapped in their golden handcuffs. Decent job, house, girl, and before you know it you're making the same drive to work five days a week for forty years. Hair cut & mow the lawn over and over. Spend half your vacation days each year on obligatory family functions. Spend a good chunk of savings on home projects and some necessities for the kids. Fast forward to old age. I'm
207

watching it happen to everyone I know. I'm way up high in the Rockies, or bouncing around the globe avoiding that whole thing.

I gather from my conversation with Joe that Rich is really holding the place down. Apparently, he went through a whole checklist with Joe about the upcoming lawn and appliance projects that will be coming due this summer. I picture him wearing a badge and a cape. Truly his father's son... like everyone else.

Joe tells me that Ma is making him show her five job applications each week, or else he's kicked out of the house. Such a weird threat to hold over someone's head. I ask him where he'll go if that happens. He tells me that he didn't hit her quota last week but she said that "all my boys are always welcome in my house". He was as dumbfounded as me considering our present state of affairs. It makes me wonder who my real mom is. It reminds me of that old joke where Jesus, or Matthew, or God, or one of those cartoon characters said something to the effect of "I never knew you; depart from me, you workers of lawlessness". It's not right the way that she treats me. Steve is dead and she doesn't have to keep up this narrative that I am the root of all the family's problems. It's on her to change that now.

Can't run from it anymore ole gal. Times are changing. Not the same pieces on the board as there used to be. You're the queen now, time to start acting like one. Maybe get Rich off the tit and stop acting like a kept woman. Those days are over.

I have a renaissance of self-confidence that enables me to sleep with a new woman. We start rolling with each other by chance, basically because of mutual friends we meet up with at this week's free concert. She sort of brushes her body against my arm and I think how nice this is, I can't remember the last time my skin touched another woman's skin. Fast forward a couple hours and she's pulling my hands all over her tight body on a dance floor. Then a couple hours after that I'm back at her place and she's all curled up on me. I try to just enjoy it assuming that this is just a passing mistake on her part.

This little cookie crumb. I believe her name is Tiffany. Tiny, slim, 29. Really neat to listen to. She sort of mumbles or chirps, and sort of sounds like she has a stuffy nose. She likes to color she says... like in coloring books. She's not kidding, I see them on her coffee table in the morning. Imagine that. I'm sure she's a disaster waiting to happen. I think I know two of her ex-boyfriends. And she might have a couple other boyfriends going in rotation right now too.

I'm on tilt like a sidewinder today. I don't take shit from people. Anyone. And I let em know. They send me home from work early. Maybe I'm fired, but who the fuck cares. I'm coming unglued man. Well, that's just a perception. And it has no bearing on anyone else but me, and I barely matter. I am accountable only to my dreams. I live on an island. There are no fish because my island is made of land. There is no dirt because my land is made of sand.

Maybe last night's romantic interlude boosted my ego just enough to call out my dick bag new boss in front of the crew. Regardless, last night was great. I mean, no big deal really, we basically just slept; but wrapped up in each other in her bed. So comfortable. The more the years go by, the more I appreciate the simple comfort of a girl's head laying on my chest. And also raucous sweaty loud passionate sex. I don't know though, for some reason I don't like to arrive at that climax right away. I think the slow play is vital for sustained happiness with a partner.

I wake up to an odd note that I must have written to myself last night:

Stunning, drubbing, drinking. A pup, a pin. Mint. Fourth participle. Gin. Murphy. Next.
Begin again.
And then,
And then...

What the hell did I do last night? Oh yeah, Ha! It was the funniest thing... I was smoking pot out of a page of literature. I didn't have a pipe or anything, so I used the first thing I could find. As I Lay Dying by William Faulkner. I tore out the title page and smoked that. It was so funny, so dramatic. One discolored page with only the typed words "As I Lay Dying". I rarely smoke by myself, but my neighbor grows the stuff and gave me a couple nugs the other day. I guess when I got home from the bars at 2 am piss drunk I decided that it would be a great idea to smoke it up. A funny fuzzy memory.

The waterfall across the street from my front porch is barely more than a trickle now that the snow on the mountain is mostly melted. Cookie crumb seems to have crumbled. Haven't heard back from her since that night. I ponder this latest failed love of about five days ago in conjunction with all the rest. Who knows what her deal was. Something. Scars. We all have them and have to work around each others'. I think I only fixate on this girl right now because of her zero response. Nothing. Is she dead I wonder? Maybe her phone, internet, and stuff like that are all out of order. Most likely she has seven other dudes in orbit, and a bag full of abortions she walks around with all day. Something like that, unspoken but felt, that made me interested in the first place. I can feel her lostness, and I like it.

I guess I'll try to go to the mental doctor tomorrow so that we can take turns trying to figure out what's wrong with me. Partially cloudy. 79°

An Irish hoot

I believe that I have no idea what's going on. I hope Brixton doesn't find out and have me assassinated. After a series of miscues, I snap and have another episode at the start of my shift. I'm having a fine day moving furniture and setting up for an event when one of the tables I'm moving falls apart, and I have a full blown temper tantrum. The table was supposed to have been fixed two weeks ago when a couple other people almost fucked themselves up moving it. Not really a big deal, but I lose my shit. I start cursing and throwing about a dozen chairs around the room. I go to the office to raise hell, and one of the senior managers fires back at me about my level of disrespect. She is usually as much of a cunt as I'm being right at this particular moment, so we storm off together to report the incident to the poor bastard who happens to be sitting in the safety office.

I think it's ok to go ape shit as long as your intentions are pure. Basically, I acted like a woman that found a marble in her vacuum cleaner. Everyone was concerned and perplexed, so in the end, I guess I redeemed some sort of street cred because I'm a feminist. There is a pleasant calm after the storm in my mind and I go back to setting up the wedding dinner. But my co-workers saw for maybe the first time that I am a complete sociopath. It's hard to describe what it feels like to reside behind a stone cold gaze in moments of rage. I have the strength of ten men while my affect is nil. Check my paperwork from Norristown, it's true. All my observers in their deep subconscious knew that behind my cold gaze is a robot that would be equally unphased polishing a wine glass or ripping your throat out of your neck. They are both such very simple tasks.

You should have been there in Pensacola 2001. Officer school is a very deliberate training regimen. Probably developed by Napoleon, refined by Hitler, and studied by gunnery sergeant Merryman. He had a tattoo of a boy with a balloon on his calf, but he was a hard ass mother fucker. We probably would have had a great mentor / protégé relationship if it wasn't for my utter contempt of authority. Also, they're not too keen on humor in the corps. The act that sprung me loose was basically a

211

quote from Forrest Gump that I dropped in front of the tribe to his silly remark about polishing a belt buckle. Stupid is as stupid does. I think the troop thought he was going to shoot me right there on the spot. I knew he wouldn't though. It's against the rules. He knew it and I knew it. Montgomery 1, Merryman 0. I wonder what happened to the rest of that class. I got cut at around week 3 out of 13. It was right before that hilarious joke when the airplanes tipped over all the cubicles in the big apple. I wonder if I technically qualify as a veteran of the military. I betchya I do.

Anyway after my little episode this morning, the guests arrive at the hotel, and the event is a success. The father of the groom gives a very touching speech. I tell him that I work these types of events all the time and that his speech was terrific. It was a great speech from a quiet man with a humble white mustache. I always like to listen to the toasts. My life revolves around toasts. It's very nice. I see all these people come together from all around the world for weddings. I watch them all interact and observe the miracle of holy or civil matrimony. It's nice to attend their parties and eat their food without the obligation of having to interact with any of them unless I chose to bless them with the treasure of passed gourmet appetizers and the open ear of a mysterious mountain dweller. It's a nice gig.

I'm still not exactly sure why I went completely insane today. It's funny that there are no repercussions. In real places, a person gets fired on the spot at point blank range for that kind of behavior. But most of the people that live in Vail are complete bums. So basically as long as you show up for most of your shifts, and aren't often visibly intoxicated, you're fine. It also helps the longevity of your career in these parts if you have no aspirations of advancing to a level of leadership. All the leaders are women.

Besides this morning I've been in a great state of mind for as long as I can remember. I think that maybe I was thrown off kilter when that bomb robot killed the sniper that shot all those cops in Dallas because he was upset about all the black men that the cops are always shooting for basically no reason. It was in the news, did you see it? Strangest story ever; a real turning point in humanity.

These race riots all seem like a simple issue - standard historical anecdotes of disparity between government coddled aristocrats and the poor. Standard up-rise of strong people with nothing to lose that only justifies the damned and further incriminates the innocent. But then a robot kills the people's hero, and the gentle souls are participating in fancy time while the icebergs melt and the children of Sudan take up arms in the diamond mines and oil fields. And also my table fell apart today.

Progressing on toward a very drunken state again at 3 am mountain standard time. I'm drinking wine out of a box. It's what I do almost every night. Coffee through the day, beer if I have the day off and find myself in town, then a few hours of imbibing that sweet sweet grape mash. It's the best. Especially if it's the expensive box wine. It's smooth. It's the Natural Light of wine. When you're drinking from a box there's really no way to tell how much you've had unless sometimes when you wake up at noon still completely hammered. So yeah, that's kind of where my life is these days.

It's funny, I've started to realize that on many days I don't utter a single word. Often, if I don't go to work, I don't interact with anyone. It's become kind of funny to me to realize as I lay my head down at night that I haven't made a single sound out of my face all day. Totally silent. I kind of realized it one day, then thought about how it wasn't really that obscure of a day. I've come to realize that on days that I'm not working, it's pretty much 50/50 whether I will utter a single word. I only realized it a few weeks ago, but looking back it's been like that for at least a year. When I do speak in social settings it's obvious that I'm not normal. I try. People try to relate, but I usually just end up running laps around their heads till they get frustrated. I really can't help it. I basically have a bar I go to for that nonsense, another bar for sports, and another bar to listen to live music.

But mostly I just stay home these days in my little studio apartment.

It's too bad there's no chick here to wake up with. It really is a nice place. My Chinese bamboo blinds are permeable and only half block the light, so you can see the natural surroundings outside very clearly. It gets bright early in the morning. From where my head lays I look over my feet and see a meniscus of mountain with the blue sky above it. All the leaves are yellow this morning. Yesterday when I woke up they were mostly green. Funny how all the trees decide at once when it's time to do things like change colors. It's the nicest morning to laze around, but I can't totally enjoy it from bed because I have to be at work at noon. I hit the snooze button several times between 10 and 11 to try and finish the dreams I'm having. They're all over the place. Hopefully I can finish them up tonight.

The only people I talk to now are people at work. But, since I'm waist deep in a spiraling breakdown of depression I think it's getting awkward for everyone. I'm studying the corn on the cob I'm eating, looking at its molecules, when one of the guys I work with says, "Are you ok man? You look… sad."

When you've been sinking lower and lower for days, and someone says something like that, the panic sets in. When you're worried that people can tell, and you try real hard to act normal, but then catch a glimpse of yourself in the mirror and realize your eyes are bugging out of your skull, that's when you know it's falling apart again. What the hell am I doing here? I guess maybe I'll go back to the doctor and get my blood looked at and maybe they'll find something; like a biologic molecule that's jamming up my membranes. I'll hope for it, but how can I believe in hope. It's just a matter of time now. And that's fine.

It's been said that barbed wire was the most transformative invention in America. Before that everything walked basically wherever it wanted. Nomad animals walking with the seasons. Then, all of a sudden, everyone had to stop in the middle of the wide open world and turn around. How confusing that must have been.

On my grandfather's death day a bunch of us uncles and cousins got together at the farm to round up some of the cows. We were segregating the heifers from the calves when one of the calves jumped over the barbed wire fence. Clear over it, practically 5 feet high. Uncle John said he'd never seen that before. Now he tells that story every time we're all around. Gosh, I can hear him now. You should hear Uncle John tell stories. One after another at the family gatherings. Everyone has heard them all already, but they're just so fun to listen to anyway. I would describe it as an Irish hoot.

Old Toe

Maybe something fantastic has happened and nobody has told me yet. Big secret. I wonder what the secrets are these days. So unimpressive. There is a poison lotus in the attic, and I am a common house fly. Or no, that's not right. I live with 5 suns in a terrarium on Roxbury Avenue. 2 are duds, one a white dwarf, and there is also a twin helix. The telegram reads "Boat sprung leak, need gas whenever". I don't know what any of that means. I wonder if I even live in the Rocky Mountains. Maybe I'm trapped in a terrarium, paralyzed from the eyebrows down and I'm fooling myself into thinking that I wake up and go to work whenever seems appropriate day to day, then I wander this planet when the seasons change. I just don't know if I'm real. I mean, I think I'm dead and dreaming but don't totally realize it yet. I mean, obviously I have some sort of sense of reality about the situation since I'm writing it, but I think I'll still go about this existence as someone who eats, sleeps, and breaths. One day though...

I feel like I'm getting close, but at the same time, I feel it all slipping away. But I'm ok with it because I don't really have much, and I'm not really here wherever I am. So "it slipping away" doesn't really have that much importance. I have to go now. My dreams are calling for me. Death is only one day closer than it was yesterday at this time.

So, maybe I'll ski another season, maybe visit New Zealand, but soon after that, I think I'll be done gallivanting around like the Prince of Whales. I'll trim a little mustache and overdress for a dull office job in a nearby metroplex. I might take for my own a down-on-her-luck girl from the town of Franklin. I'm pretty sure there is a Franklin Township in every state in the union. We'll name our first kid Franklin if it's a boy. But it'll be a girl. You can always tell what kind of seed a man lays. I lay eggs. Brown eggs that sit out in the sun.

My ultimate problem is the anger I am unable to let go of. It's something I try to do, but can't. Some people try to do math, but just can't. Bro Joe can hold a hell of a grudge too. He hasn't spoken to brother Vin in about 15 years. Longest grudge ever. The parallels between that and the beef between me and the Knight Commander are astounding. Joe, like myself, has no problem taking the Cool Hand Luke approach of letting the world beat you down with ignorance knowing that with every swing they take they have to reaffirm the lies they tell themselves. I guess the hope for people like us is that their conscience and reason win out over the evil manifestation of self-delusion. Something like that. My ideas are getting too grand to properly apply to the present situation... Except that's all I can do.

My head spins and spins on this. I wake up in the middle of the night thinking about it. During the day my mind is usually between 30 and 70 percent focused on this busted relationship. For weeks I've been trying to figure a good person to ask about how to stop fixating on this thing. I don't want to bring people down about it, or further expose myself as damaged goods with a mommy issue.

Ma is the opposite of Cool Hand Luke - not the boss that beats him, but rather the drones that follow all the bosses. She follows bosses. Don was a boss. Rich is a boss in the most hilarious, pathetic, ironic way possible. So that's comforting. Joe... he thinks he wants to be a boss, but he also has a similar contempt for the system of human hierarchy as I do, but to a lesser extent I'd say. He'll work his way right into it though. It'll be very interesting to see how his story unfolds. The weakness that mom and I and Joe share is a stubbornness in our convictions. We know our truths to be right, and will not get off that. The problem is that when the truth you have always known turns out to be a lie, well, then there is a fork in the road.

I'm coming off my recent wave of mania with a show-stopping depression. Maybe today will be better. I'd rather lay in bed for the next 5 days. I'll need doctor's orders to do that and get away with it. Gosh, they used to keep the nut house so cold all the time. And the blankets were paper thin. And the other nuts were always screaming and banging their head on the walls. I think I miss it a little. Maybe I'll go back. It wouldn't be the same though. Maybe it would. Maybe it will.

I like this wave of depression because it hasn't been accompanied with the frenzy of nervous panic. I'm just sleeping a lot, not wanting to get out of bed even though it's 2 pm. Beautiful weather outside. Blooming pre-autumn crisp air. Leaves rustling. Dogs chasing. Maybe I'm inadvertently living the Buddhist mantra of having no desires and letting the world spin around me. Maybe I'm finally just accepting everything as it is.

I make my way to the ole cafe. It's become my standard pastime. I should be doing more in this mountainous wonderland, but I don't. I don't know, I'm comfortable here. It's like sitting on the beach - another activity I don't really understand. But who cares. I came to the conclusion some years ago that it really doesn't matter what you do 95% of the time. The only things that really have any bearing on the pattern and path of a person's life happen by random chance. So trying is kind of futile. I have found that it is generally best to get out once in a while in strange places to sort of shake up the snow globe and see which flakes bump around.

These ladies walking by - 50-year-olds with prominent camel toes. This one is wearing yoga pants. She's probably in her late 50s or 60s. Can you imagine - she must know it's all on display. I forgot to look for a wedding ring. That's a clue to the eternal mystery. So she's old but is following the fashion of the time by shaving it bald. That wasn't ever a thing when I was in college. It was pretty much unheard of before the porn revolution. I read somewhere that porn accounts for around 25% of Internet traffic. I believe it. A third of that is women viewing smut and erotica.

Here comes another one. She's wearing slacks, so it's harder to tell, but as she passes there is no doubt; it's a toe. I have reflective sunglasses on so it doesn't really matter if I take a good look. I can tell she either has a g-string or no panties at all. She has these ridiculous pants pulled up so tight it's just... I don't know. Imagine the audacity, an older lady strutting around like that. My theory is that she's doing a diddle strut. That's what I'm calling it when the inseam flicks the lady's clit bean back and forth with each stride. I heard a girl talk about this move before. She said if it starts happening you just keep on walking girl. Is this a sick fascination of mine? I don't think so. Just a mysterious thing. It's ok to observe the mating habits of humans I think. I'm a feminist. I saw a girl at my pool the other day sitting in the hot tub with the jets on, and she was facing the outside. She sort of hovered horizontally and the jet stream was pushing out her bikini bottoms. Can you imagine? Right there in front of everyone, like a dog humping a teddy bear. A public diddle. No shame. She's my age and very attractive. Her older bald boyfriend had been stroking her hair a minute earlier. They were talking as she was doing the tub bubble diddle. Girls are really getting bold these days. I think they're letting their recent world domination go to their heads.

My bass and guitar sit in the corner of my studio apartment collecting dust. I should buy one of those pedals where you can sort of loop the beat, and play along with yourself. I guess I just want to waste my time playing with myself in more productive ways than I currently am. I'm bored with going out to bars etc. I'm always solo because I have yet to make a good friend like that here. It's only been 5 years though, maybe I just need to give it time. If I died of a heart attack, and didn't have to be at work, I doubt anyone would know until the neighbors complained about the stench. I don't think I'm alone in that state of living. I'm just one of those lost souls. No big deal. I'm basically nobody like nobody else.

Nights are getting pretty cold here now. 40s. Crisp air. Today was the first day of actual fall. I don't give a god damn what the Hallmark calendar says. Mom told me that somebody died yesterday, so our relationship is gravitating around an orbit again. Did you know that there's a planet between Mars and Jupiter that hasn't formed yet? Yes, it's the asteroid belt! It just hasn't really collected its debris together yet, but by the power of math and science we know that it basically occupies its orbit the same as the other 9 planets... well, 8 anyway. We lost Pluto to cold space during the Obama years.

In an effort to cope with... life, I think it's time for me to abandon reason. I need to pray to and put my faith in a higher power. What would that form of god be though? I need to invent one that fits with everything I've come to believe is true. The reality that we are all one, but simultaneously all utterly alone. "We" is an imaginary term. A person can't truly perceive another person. Or maybe they can, I don't know. Either way, the standard religious deduction from this point is that god must be at the center of a person's life, above all else even wife, friends, family, children.

Science, particularly astrophysics and quantum physics just don't add up yet. The fact that we live in middle of it and can't fit those two polarities together in our limited view of space-time is all the proof I need to show that we are way off in the way we are defining our existence. So that's sort of my best internal version of the mystery of heaven and hell. Like the abstract multi-dimensions described in string theory. I suppose it takes faith in the number system. But there are no numbers inside the gates of Eden. I don't know about angels and violins in heaven. I don't believe in that kind of fantasy stuff. I believe in space, and the theories I have heard about the multiverse. So in a way, I guess I believe that there is another copy of myself that believes in heaven and will, therefore, go to heaven. But that's just an equation.

Then you have the more concrete adaptations of faith. Surrender to good will, forgiveness, charity, and other affirmative social constructs. Maintain selflessness and humility. And just hope that in your time of need some stranger will sacrifice as much of himself to help you. I'd have to accept the reality now though that it probably wouldn't happen, and that I'll feel like a fool having to bounce myself up off the bottom again. I believe I have exactly one more left. I guess I'm just waiting for the right opportunity to lose everything one more time.

When the judges and doctors kept sentencing me to more and more incarcerations in the nut houses and jails in 2001 and 2005 they always threw around this term "302" which was basically the official designation for involuntary admission to a nut house.

All of us patients/convicts knew what it meant. With no crime committed you could be locked up without trial if two people in your circle of dependents turn you over to the authorities. Kids, parents, spouses, roommates, partners, companions - ya know, the loved one's you should be able to trust the most. Well at one point they were going to 306 me. That would have given them the authority to keep me for 4 to 6 months. After that, I'd have been dog food. It's a wonder I made it out of a month of solitary confinement especially since that time was sandwiched between 302's back in Brixton.

Oooo boy. I can feel one of my favorite kinds of depressions coming on now. The numb kind. Zero affect. Affect I believe is a term that basically describes facial expression. It's the face that cold hard psycho killers make. Not that that's me, it's just a point of reference. But I think that's why they almost kept me locked up forever. I'm never going back there alive. I'll skin myself.

There's a sense that I dredge this stuff up for self-pity or attention or to play the victim for reasons of self-righteousness. That's what they say about rape victims and black men serving decades for petty crimes. They say the person basically brought it on themselves one way or another. And the devil laughs and laughs. Hilarious. Who's gonna trace these things back fifteen years? So many variables. So easy to cover the trail.

And so, all I can do is abandon reason...

This isn't just a particular chapter in history that I obsess over. I live through hells constantly. Terrible pains I drag around while functioning in this world with my remaining ten percent of strength. And don't even get me started on the prescription pills. Tranquilizers. How does my soul move through this void? What pact did I make with the devil all those years ago? Can I ever take it back, un-sign the book? They were right. I should have been locked up permanently.

What a sticky position I put everyone in back then. It's true. I know I don't fully realize, only observe the fallout. I think I'm pretty good at diagnosing modus operandi. As for my own, at that time... It's very complicated. Very very complicated.

I guess I was out of control and tough to be around. But like I said, I'm a feminist. I make impulsive decisions that put everyone on the spot. I judge their reactions. I express my judgments in a way that either challenges them to be better or punishes them to walk themselves to hell. They're passive acts that I let happen by obeying instincts. And I walk right down to hell with them.

The moral hazard of religion

I remember being in her kitchen as a child in the nineties listening to Limbaugh and being so frustrated at how his twisted logic warped her opinions. More recently I was a caretaker for a ninety-year-old man with dementia who watched Fox News all day. I was just as frustrated because I knew the same facts that the pundits did, and I could see them lie through their teeth about them day in and day out. Seeing that network get him so riled up by feeding on his born privilege and racism, and studying how those pundits and networks got their money and influence was absolutely sickening.

I wonder if conservative Republican news consumers like them know that in the last 8 years our country's unemployment rate has been cut in half. Do they realize that we no longer have a dozen dead soldiers coming home every single day from bogus wars propagated on lies, and do they appreciate that we haven't fallen into the trap of following temptation's page into a new war just like the last? Have they seen that gas prices are half what they were as US oil production has doubled? The stock market too has doubled. 20 million more people have health insurance and will no longer bankrupt their families seeing a doctor or buying the pills they are prescribed. Wages are up, crime is down, and nobody had their guns taken away. And whether they understand science or not, the sun does not revolve around the earth, and the planet is getting warmer.

The dire predictions and minute by minute accounts of Obama's presidency could not have been more false. But still a wide swath of Americans, her included, continue to validate these deceptions, and trust that what their leader Donald Trump is telling them is the truth. The monster that the Republican propaganda machine has created with decades of misinformation, fear, hate, and ignorance is eating that institution alive. These poison ideas are plain to hear in the voices of so many of his followers; people that have based their view of the world on the same media sources that you have for so long. I don't believe they are all racists, but doesn't it give them pause when they hear the bigotry, ignorance, and aggressive nature of people supporting the same leader? I ask myself, what kind of mental gymnastics do intelligent people of faith have to do to stay in line with an institution that has gone so rotten, and support a man that so clearly embodies all things evil in this world.

Although I don't buy into the standard Christian doctrine as it is presented these days, I did take away some good lessons from my time in the religious community. After twelve years of Catholic school, I served as a Eucharistic minister, a lector, and prison minister all through college. It's not religion that I despise, its hypocrisy, and it is hiding like a flock of lambs in plain sight everywhere. Hypocrisy is one of the most referenced evils in the Bible besides idolatry and the idea of being owned by your possessions.

I have no real interest in the outcome of this silly presidential race that everyone has been watching for the last four years. Nothing is really decided on an election day anyway, and the campaign for the next cycle starts 30 seconds after the winning party is declared. What I watch is the movement of the masses, and I listen to how individuals of different opinions express and defend themselves. It pains me to see people close to me stay aboard a sinking ship and go down in flames believing the lies that deep inside they know they are being told. I think that no matter what a person's political or spiritual affiliation, they owe it to themselves and to their god to use the mind they were given to seek truth and call out the lies - particularly of the man-made institutions in which they place their faith and loyalty. History and the Bible provide countless examples of what happens when people let themselves be misled by evil forces and shelter their conscience with denial, deflection, and propagation of those blatant lies. Second Epistle of Peter chapter 2, and Second Thessalonians 2:9-11. If you have a Bible handy, check it out.

What do you do if your whole school, family, society, etc. was very proud of the person you have made yourself and the good righteous role you're playing in the world, and you live a long healthy life passing on these traditions to a strong proud line, only to eventually realize that you are basically serving an evil hand - like a Nazi, a drug dealer, a weapon manufacturer, or a Christian in the crusades? Before the institutions fell and all associated with it went down in history as villains, for a while they were doing what they thought was right, and they were doing it their best. It is a part of a human condition to realize that something you tried hard to be better at for the sake of good is actually causing more harm the better you are at it. This is where a person chooses good or evil I think. Do you choose ignorance for the sake of mental comfort, or change direction back upstream? It's like if you realize that being a great farmer is inadvertently melting the ice caps. If you realize it and say - I don't care, I'm doing it anyway... that's fine because you acknowledged it and chose your choice. If you see and understand the facts, but then actively deny them, and join with others that will support each other's group ignorance, well, then you're being a bad Nazi.

We can fight every single day for what we believe in. I don't think it will do us any good. So why do we do it anyway? I do it because it makes me feel alive. The fight isn't about hurting anyone, or for personal glory. There is an evil out there - an ignorance. I feel like it's my duty to point it out, expose it, and condemn it, even when it causes me such personal loss and isolation. That was a big piece of my nut house tours. I spit in the face of the status quo ignorant close minded temples of institution. The members of this operation know deep down they are part of something evil. Something counter to human advancement. There is always a force in our species that enslaves people's minds, bodies, and souls. False reason manufactured I suppose by the devil himself perhaps.

Often, the evil has invaded places that people hold in the safest, highest regards. Church is an easy one. Everyone sees church differently I think. As children, like many others, we were taught that prayer is right, heaven is real, and priests are close enough to god that we must trust them and their institution blindly. Obviously, this logic is flawed. Sadly, that point is missed by pretty much everyone at church on Sundays. And the dominoes fall over and over, all the way down the line. Holding up these beliefs is a reticent crusade.

This issue with ma runs pretty deep. We don't despise each other, but I think our opinions disgust each other, and we're both so stubborn in our convictions. When the convictions that you've followed in good conscience are shown to be wrong, do you listen to reason, reassess and go forward in a better direction, or do you site blind faith, righteousness, and other tools and rhetoric to intentionally confuse the issues and twist the lines around right and wrong? Are you strong enough to listen to the voice in your head telling you something is wrong here? How hard she must have to try, and how many beads she must have to pray on to get temporary relief from that nagging feeling of cognitive dissonance.

Obviously, perceiving things this way, I recognize that I'm projecting my own insecurity in my convictions. The past is long behind, but those hospital times were the most formative in my life. Everything else pales in comparison. The way people changed and acted and spoke to me and about me in those times just exposed so much about human nature; the reality of iron bars and pills and needles as forms of humans enslaving humans. A judge or doctor makes a decision but then is detached from pleas the prisoner makes to his handlers. They don't care. They are bosses carrying out orders as best they can because they're strong in the riotousness of their actions. They trust the system and the hierarchy. Ok, it's a complicated network of people, but there are some very key players that are making decisions that... Blah blah blah. We've heard this whole song and dance before. What am I not allowing myself to acknowledge and accept with all this dispersal of blame at unanimous ghosts? Shoot, I just can't tell.

The line between family values and political viewpoints is just so interwoven that it's almost impossible to describe without sounding completely neurotic. The luxury I have though is that I've already been exposed as clinically insane. If my words make any sense, you might also be insane, or perhaps the clinic itself is misaligned with the truth. I obviously think the latter.

I believe that emotions and opinions born out of fear and ignorance are evil - specifically when they're intentionally propagated, and not begotten unknowingly. A politician that knowingly goes along with something he or she knows is a mistruth is a tool of evil. They may fool themselves into believing their untruths are for a good cause, but lies and misinformation set our species back. The ripple effect of these propagated lies ruins lives.

I think the word "politics" closes people's mind sometimes. You can't talk about it in certain places. Is talking about history, sociology, psychology any different at this point? It's a harsh reality, but we're in a fragile point of human existence right now. The knowledge may end up getting lost like in the dark ages, or we may move to a time of awakening. This current situation with Trump... I don't know how it stacks up against some of history's other blunders, but it's a notable happening. A lot of people don't even see it. Some see it only from the lies they're being fed. That's sad, but it's just the way it is. The worst part of this type of occurrence are the people that have been propagating what they thought was the truth for what they used to think was a good cause. They see it for what it is now, but they can't bring themselves to acknowledge it. That is where denial, self-deception, cognitive dissonance come in. There are lives like a row of dominoes knocked down in the wake of this evil.

Many see the monster that has been created. Some don't see it at all, and are consumed by it. Some though, some continue to knowingly serve the lies because they won't let themselves admit they were fooled. These are the ones that have it the worst. The amount of mental energy it takes to maintain the self-delusion, and knowing spread evil rather than admit defeat, it consumes people. It's sad to watch. Some of these people know they are exposed. For example, mom knows I'm aware of the levels of ignorance she cloaks herself in to keep up the appearance of a good Christian American widow.

Many of us know and accept that money is the root of all evil. From there we can have many different opinions about the way that evil presents itself into out reality. Wealthy people often condemn those on welfare for example. It's especially irritating to listen to these people complain when, for whatever reason, they haven't worked at an actual job in a decade or so. But they allow themselves not to see that because to do so would implicate themselves as holders of the evil that is money. But if you see the lies for what they are and go along with it anyway, winking at guy across the table as you sign the contract, well, that's propagation of the evil.

What ma doesn't know is that the pharmaceutical industry is perhaps the most evil institution of our generation. It works hand in hand with the insurance industry that leeches on our society by creating a divide between caregivers and those in need. These practices enslave the most vulnerable and hold them and their loved ones hostage to abstract obstacles of paperwork while taking trillions of dollars for the service of navigating the chasm they have created.

The pharmaceutical industry sits on top of this mess by using the oldest trick in the book - the hope of a cure at any cost. Everyone walking in the door of a doctor's office or hospital gets prescribed something. They make the consumer believe that to not pay is to surrender and say you don't care about the loved ones you choose not to save. We all participate. Some win more years and don't lose the farm doing it, but most slowly go bankrupt till their dying day. She's not dumb though, so maybe she does know how this all works. The Knight Commander was pretty high up the chain there. They don't pay you millions of dollars if you don't see the big picture and help steer the ship.

They're selling chemical compounds, and often times they are known to be poisons. The clinicians and scientists know something is amiss but the paycheck needs to cover the cost of their medical school. The school is funded by the pharmaceutical company looking for legal validation of their next million dollar super drug. The traditional symbol of a doctor is literally a staff with a snake crawling up it. The symbol for the pharmaceutical industry is a staff with two snakes crawling up it. How much more obvious can it be? Hiding in plain sight is the devil himself. It's so easy to allow yourself to be a boss in this business. You can use any number of tricks to take the paycheck and keep the machine moving forward. You can make the numbers move the facts in whatever direction you want if you're a Knight Commander of this group. You can be secure in your righteousness wearing the cross on your chest for all to see.

I know what I know, and I feel what I feel. I understand exactly how possessed and vindictive I sound with this endless pursuit of mine. Tying all these pieces together can seem insane, but my diagnosis is based on sound sociological, psychological, historical, and economic realities. It's to be expected that these ideas are confusing and that I can't yet express them fully. I guess this is just me polishing it all up before my untimely death. But it's all real. It's as real as astrophysics. We don't all have to fully understand how a black hole works. But we all instinctively have this belief in the possibility of time travel. Long ago there was fear and wonder about fire until its mysteries we're tamed. Still, it's a fluid random projection of electrons from some mysterious force in our multiverse. There really is no need to tie it to the idea of time travel, but you can't deny that it exists right next door to black holes. It's a given that they're both happening at the same time, but our expanding minds still perceive them as vastly different entities. The non-duality of these forces, and of each other is lost on most of ourselves, but it's in there somewhere, not to be denied just because it's snack time and rent is due at the end of the week.

Thought dreams

What it comes down to, the only thing that really matters is the people you have in your life. A friend, a wife, kids, a confidant, parents maybe, a pet. A million dollars means nothing if you have nobody. And being poor... well, poor sucks. I'm pretty poor these days. It's sad. I have nothing.

Work is getting tedious, but I think things are slowing down. I was thinking of going to New Zealand for a month, but I don't know if I feel like it. Maybe this fall I'll take a few road trips around some of the parts of Colorado that I haven't seen yet... which is most of it. Sand dunes, Durango, Silverton, and maybe I'll just keep driving to Zion or Bullfrog. I guess I'll probably be solo. This whole solo way of life is really getting annoying. But whatever, what can I do? Maybe I won't do anything. I'm exhausted anyway.

But back to reality. I'm still not allowed at my mother's house. It becomes more apparent every day how intentionally they tried to leave me behind all those years. It's undeniable, almost comical. How much simpler it would have been if my papa didn't live a mile down the road the whole time. Being a long-lost runaway would have been nice. How could a person obsess for so long, you might ask. Because at this very moment, I am one of about a dozen children in the world who's own mother will not let him into her house. Shunned. I'm the worst of the dozen because I can't wrap my head around - why me. I must be a psychopath, the kind that can't fully see himself for what he is.

I was thinking of constructing some sort of guillotine that would allow me to chop my head off every day before I get out of bed to go to work. I pretty much start every day, lying in bed in broad daylight, looking at the hills outside the window at my feet, thinking about having a silver wedge separate my head from my body. If I could somehow do that, then go to work at my leisure, then maybe cut my head off again mid shift, and maybe once or twice after work without all the permanent consequences that usually go along with such actions, that would probably be fine. Yes, if I was somehow able to spend a year crafting a mechanism that would allow me to chop my head off whenever I felt like it that would be just fine. I'd need a time crystal I think... and a voodoo doll probably. Unfortunately, time crystals and voodoo dolls are not going to be possible, but what will be possible is additional silver slide hatchets and helium balloons. If I could rig a mechanism to drop four additional devices to sever my arms and legs, then whisk them away in the breeze, my limbs would be properly scattered. Ideally, each limb would go on a timed release into different wind patterns. And if my head could somehow get into outer space, maybe with some sort of rocket propulsion that would be great.

It's all possible. It's possible. It's a possible endeavor. A great way to end one's life. A secret construction of a space rocket air balloon guillotine with chum mincing capability. I figure that as long as I have a few thousand dollars, and about 6 months' time I can construct a suicide mechanism that will send my body parts in different directions and my head into outer space, and the middle of my body minced to chum and sunk in a sea. I need to tell Sir Isaac Newton that if there were some sort of electromagnetic ion propulsion device that could be integrated into my guillotine, then we could...

Wait, I'm going to need a few test subjects probably. Mice. Large mice. Mice the size of grown men. I need to get a letter to the pharmaceutical industry letting them know that I need large mice... Damn. My only contact there is a dead Knight Commander and I have neither the time, ability, or desire to contact it.

Installed in the solitary confinement cells of many jails are these stainless steel toilet/sink units. They're very hollow and make for great drums. When I checked in to the box that would be my dwelling place for the next several weeks I took inventory of the situation. It was a very limited inventory. Mattress, walls, door, stainless steel apparatus, slot in the door where they insert a tray of food three times each day.

It wasn't ideal but it was better than the general population block they had me on with the rapists and murderers. I was getting some unwanted attention from one of the alphas there, and one of the guys recommended that I threaten suicide in order to get moved off the block before I get beat up. I didn't know they moved you to solitary. So it was just me and my shiny gray apparatus. If there was a small flat gray shiny razor blade lying flat on the sink, it would be hard to overlook. Well, there was one. It was an interesting moment and an interesting next few days as I used the blade to shave my chest and sideburns. The convenient setting and opportunity for suicide were obvious. It almost seemed intentional that the razor was left there. Looking back, I think that most likely it was left there by the last tenant when he was allowed to leave after who knows how many weeks or months.

Such a limited inventory I had in that tiny room. Basically one item. And from a certain perspective, it was the closest thing I had to a key out of that place that I, from a certain perspective, still dwell in this day. I think that deep down I embrace death. I think my ultimate struggle is that I only get to die once in this realm. It's a finish line. A completion.

But suicide is boring unless you build your own guillotine. Slow death... well, I haven't really thought too much about that, but it gives me comfort to know that the last miserable 20 years of a standard life take as long as these pivotal 20 years that I'm in now. Age 25 to 45 takes as long as 65 to 85. Wait... hold on a sec. My middle 20 years of life are almost up. They flew by and nothing happened. It'll be interesting to see how my life looks from age 45 to age 65.

A person going through that life stage a hundred years ago would have observed vaudeville, mass production of cars, interesting newspapers, and a collapse of society that left no food on the shelves in the grocery stores because of a calamity in some abstract thing called the stock market. A person going through that life stage fifty years ago would have just gotten done with the Vietnam conflict. Hippies were dancing around naked, TV turned to color somehow, and people went to the moon in the sky, all because of this abstract thing called the computer.

I talked to my dad. He is sad that I won't stay at his pad. I feel bad, but mom makes me mad. She thinks Rich is rad, and that dead Don is glad. I knew this was all just a fad from the time I was a lad till the day I was a grad. But now I'm had in the Sea of Chad.

I guess I'm going to have to go back to Brixton at some point and take care of my ole pa. Pricks be damned... damned to hell. And if hell won't take em... well, hell be damned. Fuck hell dude! Awe man, if I went back to Brixton and all my old friends started taking care of their dads too, and I figured out how to skateboard, and we all started a band... Dude, what if Tom's runaway dad was loaded and died and gave all his money to our band and we could all play video games and jam in his basement all day and totally be millionaires together. Fuck yeah, man!

I met with my wife today. She's banging everyone else I think, but it's still nice to talk to her. She has a pretty face to look at still, but her body isn't giving gracefully to the demands of time. I'm sure she can still snowboard like a champion, but I suspect she'll lose a limb this year. Either her or myself. I'm sorry, it's not polite to talk about myself in the royal first person... except maybe to the very next person I meet. I'm very charming you see. Unassuming, intelligent, quietly desperate with nothing to lose, and a casual wit that both appeals to and repulses everyone. Good luck I tell them. Good luck, and goodnight.

The curse of the goat

I might hop in my car and drive in a direction this week. North maybe.
West, south, or east are also just as likely I suppose. Nobody can stop
me anymore, it's great. And nobody captures me when I get back
either, which is nice. It's very comfortable to sleep in the back of my
Tahoe. When I put the back seats down I can fit a queen size mattress
back there. So I'll probably drive around in my bedroom this fall. I also
just thought the other day that maybe I'll go to Canada for a little bit. I
could drive around northern Colorado, park my bedroom in Denver
and fly to Montreal. I don't know anyone in Montreal, but I'm sure I'd
make a new acquaintance on my way from the airport to town as I'm
holding my backpack, gazing out the window, then looking at my map,
then gazing out the window again.

So tomorrow... today... later this very hour or one of the next, I will
wake up and move in a direction. I'll have no obligation for the next
four days. An average American drives 45 minutes to work each day,
and 45 back, so in order to stay average I should drive around 400
miles on the interstate this week. That leaves only four possible states
to visit. What's the one north of here? I haven't been there yet. If my
curiosity itches me I should probably go there before the season gets
too cold. Dakota? Idaho? Montana? What's the one right above me?
The Yellowstone state I think, whichever one that is. Some barren
wasteland with nothing but trash heaps and Republicans and Indians?
I guess I'll just drive north and find out. How exciting. Tomorrow I
wake up and drive north to Steamboat. To Steamboat!

I'm so full of shit, a loser, a total loser. I've lost everything over and
over, dipped out of life so many times, and now I have nothing. I play
video games. I go outside sometimes if I can summon up the
motivation to do something besides go to work. I work for a company.
I set up chairs and I clean plates of food. Then I get on planes to go to
places just to boast that I've been somewhere. But I've not even been
to where I am. I'm not even here... I'm [dramatic literary pause] out

there.

It's funny. Now that I've been here in this apartment all summer by myself, and since I don't really see people all that often except at work, I'm starting to feel like I'm on another planet. Now that I'm not working too much, I find myself staying in here all day - days at a time. Looking back, I'm starting to see this whole Colorado escapade as a lone wolf mission. And these satellite backpacking trips I've been taking are just me stepping out into the world to look around and gather clues and observations to bring back to my outpost here on my rocky mountain. I've gotten pretty good at living out of a backpack for weeks at a time on these trips, and efficiently taking creature comforts without using too many resources. Now that I have my own place, I'm just not really feeling like venturing out again.

I don't know, maybe that's not it. I feel like I'm getting stale. My summer labor is nearly over. It looks like I have one more full week of work coming up, then that will be all for a while. This week has been my first sort of trial with an open schedule since... since some part of last winter I guess. These last couple days have been wasteful. I've done almost nothing. Maybe it's just me resting and recovering. I don't know. But I sleep later and later into the afternoon lately. I'm almost never out of bed by noon... but I also don't go to bed until around 4 am usually either. Not sure what that's about. It's partially video game syndrome. It's not that I sleep too much, I just let the sun move through its pattern longer than most before I make my moves. There is a decent chance that I will pull out of this cycle this winter when I work less, and have skiing as an optional activity every day.

We'll see how things progress. I think this life of solitude is pretty much here for good now. Although, every day brings with it the possibility of a metaphorical October surprise. I went to my coffee shop today to sit out on the square and do my thing for a while. The girl asked me if I'd been away. Nope, just working I said. But in reality, I have been away. I stay in. I have no catalyst to leave my place. No catalyst for anything. I'm not anywhere else anymore. I'm away.

This Donald Trump guy, man, ya gotta love the way he just doesn't give a fuck about anything. Total lunatic. I hope he gets to be our leader. It's not looking likely, but I bet he and the devil have a last minute trick up their sleeve. The news shows have been so much more entertaining with him as a parody of himself and all things Republican. It's funny and sad at the same time, but I think every civilization just has to come to terms with the fact that there will be an uneven distribution of resources. And when that happens territory will be disputed. So you have a steady rate of casualties there... maybe it will make the colony better in a way.

I suffered another sudden sadness this evening. I left my heart out on the windowsill, and my hummingbird kicked it off the ledge. Oh well. At least I put it out there. Yes, I asked my Claire a question... basically seeing if we might, ya know, be together in some way. The answer I got back was a very decisive rejection. But I guess it's better to know where that stands then to hope and guess all winter now that she's moved back to Vail. I like hanging out with her, and she's pretty, so of course, I'd have hope of something developing there. It still always surprises me that not a single girl I go for ever really wants to be with me, especially with all the idiots out there. I've really never been able to figure that out. My grandma and I are both pretty convinced that I'm quite a catch. I'm not really upset about these things, it's just something that doesn't make sense.

I was so baffled at one point a few years ago that I thought everything would change if I had the rhinoplasty doctor cut my nose in half. Instead, I decided to walk around the Far East and nail a Jew in the ocean and write a book. And nothing changed. That led to a different imaginary storyline of future possibilities keeping my mind occupied for about a year. But that old bird kicked my heart off a ledge too. It happens - to some people more than others. No big deal I suppose. But I guess you gotta be willing to make the moves and fail. And you need to be willing to settle for some personal and physical flaws if you want a steady girl to be with. Unless you're handsome, have money, and an asshole ego. Then you pretty much get whatever you want in life.

236

I was thinking Claire would have been nice to be with because she can be such a depressed recluse sometimes like me. I pictured us just sitting around my apartment binge watching movies or football, or her reading a book while I play video games, or us playing cards or chess or board games together maybe with a few other weird people. And of course skiing together. And I thought it would be great if we took a road trip around the dessert... and traveled the world together from time to time. Don't judge me, I know it's dumb but it's my stupid hobby. She'll still be a fun mate anyway once this awkward exchange passes and one of us starts banging a new person. Yeah, I had some high hopes I had been building up in my head over the last few weeks when I found out she was moving back to Vail. The bubble burst for the best though I guess. I recognize the feeling, and I know I'll basically have the equivalent of an emotional head cold until probably Tuesday. By then my mind will have most likely moved to the next life thing.

Sports update: the Chicago Cubs have won the pennant and are headed to the World Series for the first time in approximately one million years. Legend has it that there was some sort of curse put on them involving a goat.

Down in Costa Rica this spring, when Joe was watching early season games on his cell phone, I told him that I'd meet up with him in Chicago if the squad made it to the big show. So, I guess I'll be filling up my ole orange backpack with bare minimal essentials and walking east by northeast toward Chi-town real soon.

I'm at one of those sneaky opportunities for the devil to strike. Now that the summer wedding season is over and I have no work, a period of inaction is upon me. My adapted instinct has been to plot a course into the unknown. I start looking at prices for flights out of Chicago to various global destinations. Greece, London, Canada, New Zealand - all relatively cheap, and I haven't been to any of those places. This is not the time in my life to be worrying about silly details like that though. No, at this juncture it's time for me to accept that the 6th chapter is done and it's time to move on to the next.

7

London Calling

Go Cubs Go

Although my flights to Chicago and England are already booked, I'm apprehensive about using them and I don't know why. There's a lesson I learned a while ago though - it's perfectly acceptable to pull back and fold the hand if you don't like the way the table feels. If your bishop is out of position, light the board on fire and start again. Tomorrow.

I have a great new idea. I'm going to start wearing a wedding ring. I think it'll basically just help me feel like I fit in better - like wearing a baseball cap. It's disarming. I wouldn't bring it up but should be ready with a hilarious anecdote if anyone asks... "Shark attack. My wife died in a shark attack accident in Tamarindo. She appeared to be very chewy. Her name was pneumonia and I still love her. Now please leave me alone with my thoughts. Thank you."

Cubs vs Indians. It's happening. My quest will be to meet Joe near the stadium for game 4 in Chicago. Playing video games helps me navigate and appreciate quests like this. You study maps, plot destinations, and talk to people to establish tasks, quests, and destinations. Put together a team, keep your inventory tight, rest to keep up your endurance, explore without straying too far into dangerous areas. The goal is to gain experience, retrieve rare items, and discover new worlds. And you play the game just for the heck of it. It's like landing on the moon. No need to sweat the details, because there's really no urgency about the whole operation anyway. If everything goes haywire and I end up in Phoenix, who cares. I guess I'll just go to a bar in Phoenix. That's basically worst case scenario. Actually, worst case scenario is having no place to sleep after the bars close and having no money. But that's armature shit.

I study the internet matrix and find a flight from Denver to Chicago for $80. I know nothing about the way Chicago is laid out, so I study the map online for about a half hour, then sketch a grid of my own in my journal detailing the streets near the ballpark. I mark the bars in the area so that I will have the lay of the land and an idea of where I'll probably meet Joe. My biggest challenge is figuring how to handle the fact that I'll have my travel backpack. After a little research, I find that there are lockers in Union Station. It seems out of the way, but after studying the grid for another ten minutes I realize the metro hub between the airport and the ballpark is in Union Station anyway. So, I'll land at 5 pm Central time, blue line to Union Station, drop luggage, hop back on the blue line to the ballpark, and arrive around the time they're singing the national anthem.

I have the new found energy that only comes with deployment to my next backpack trip. I've basically slept, worked, wanked, drank and played video games for this entire summer. I guess it's time to wake up and go live a little one more time.

Today is my mom's holy birthday. It's also the 115 year anniversary of day Annie Edson Taylor became the first person to go over Niagara Falls in a barrel. Also the anniversary of the stock market crash of 1929 and 2008 fyi.

I arrive in Chicago an hour before game 4 and find my way to the bar near the stadium where he and his mom Viv are watching the game. Cubs lose and go down 3 games to 1 and are on the brink of disaster. Joe holds it together pretty well considering that he's been living, breathing, and bleeding for this team his entire life.

Viv is a wild child. She's bouncing off the walls as we watch game 5. I'm getting Cubs fever too. Chapman, the Cubs closing pitcher all season, comes in to pitch in the 7th inning and rocks the tribe for three of the most epic innings of baseball I've ever seen. It's the most intense battle I've seen since that chicken fight back in Nicaragua. The Cubs chances to bring back the glory after over 100 years is still aren't looking good, but Joe, Viv, and I are having an awesome time.

Travel day for the Cubs and Indians. The World Series picks up again tomorrow in Cleveland. So, I guess it's Chicago tourist day for Shawn and Joe. As it happens, the Bears are playing a Monday Night Football home game tonight, so we pick up a couple tickets. While we're wandering around town all day we check out Sears Tower (tall), the big silver bean (shinny), Museum of Natural History (neat), and the aquarium (lame). We also take a stroll past Trump Tower just so that I can get a picture giving it the middle finger.

The Bears anthem is just as good as the Cubs anthem, and every fan sings them with gusto. Monday night - Bears win. Holy shit, that never happens. Next day - Cubs game 6... Cubs win! Holy shit, game seven is going to be amazing!!!

Oh damn, my flight to London leaves that day. I booked it thinking, what are the chances that the series goes seven games? It's an evening flight though. I should be able to catch the game from the airport.

Anyone that appreciates baseball even the slightest bit is watching this as perhaps the greatest game of all time. It is with tears in our eyes that the passengers of flight 232 from Chicago to London board the 767 in the middle of the 6th inning with the Cubs up 2 to 3. Rows 31 to 35 huddle around seat 32D to watch as much as we can on his computer screen before takeoff. Our hearts sink as Cleveland ties it up in the bottom of the 8th just before the flight attendants make us shut off our personal computer devices. Noooooo!!!!!

I'm 40,000 feet in the air floating over the Atlantic Ocean, suffering along with the rest of the gang, unable to experience the drama of every historic pitch. God Dammit. Eventually we the pilot informs us in a non-climactic fashion that the Cubs have won. Chicago must be going nuts right now. I should have skipped this flight. This trip sucks already.

The Rose and Crown

This traveling nonsense is absurd, I know, but it's just the only way I've found to cope with life. I have nothing wherever I am, so therefore there is this illusion of something somewhere else. If I'm going to be alone it might as well be in a place where I've never been. It's less depressing that way. As a solo traveler, it makes sense that I'm alone on the day I arrive, and in the hostel where I am staying. I'm still awkward as fuck, but I get better at faking it all the time. It mostly involves hiding my face in a book in the corner of a room. Watching strangers is nice, and I like listening to new ways of speaking and thinking. It's neat to see old buildings and try different food too, but that's just basically an excuse to justify going in the first place. The only real reason I do anything like this is basically just to get away from myself, but that has proven to be nearly impossible so far.

From the airplane window, I see nothing but lush rolling fertile land. It rains for at least a little bit almost every day here. The outskirts of the city consist of hundreds of castle-like estates. I'm positive they're held by the lords of the region. But even the clusters of commoner's neighborhoods that surround the city are very nicely spread out. No strip malls or sprawling parking lots around corporate campuses. There's at least a mile between neighborhoods separated by fields and woods.

All that land. So much uncrowded land once you get away from the crowd. I guess there is nice land near some crowds, but it's too crowded. Know what I mean? Yeah. Born to leave, born to stay. Whatever.

It's off season, thousands of miles from my tiny mountain town, so I'm not too surprised when I randomly bump into an acquaintance from Vail five minutes after exiting the plane. It's amazing that from a mountain town of 3,000 people, Vail locals constantly bump into each other in these foreign hubs. That this happened within 2 minutes of landing is a little ridiculous. Unfortunately, Jeff is only here in the airport making a connection from Oslo, Norway back to the states, otherwise we'd have gone straight to the pub for sure.

I have three friends from previous travels here. Kay that I met in Thailand - the retired British lady that ventures about on a regular basis. She's back here in her home port now. I partially blame her for stealing my young jewess Lee away back then, so I'm in no rush to meet up with her, but we probably will soon anyway. Then there's Flo Stow from Nicaragua. She goes to University here in the city. Quite a little whipper snapper. I'm probably older than her dad, but who cares. We're meeting up on Saturday. And finally, there's dear sweet Lenai, a complete looney toon. She's a kooky Canadian girl that I hung out with in Vail for a while until 2 years ago when she moved to London. She'll be leaving town in about a week, so I may be staying at her place if her flatmates are ok with it. People here refer to their apartments flats. Apparently, we have bastardized the origins of our English language.

Proper digs at the Rose and Crown backpacker hostel. It's a pub downstairs, with bunk dorms upstairs. I get in at around 11 am local time. It's 5 am in Chicago. Since that's the last place I woke up in I'm pretty tired at this point. The bar is open for business so I have a victory beer before going up to bed for my victory snooze. I get talking to the bartender gal from New York, then a few mid-day regulars that roll in. One of the guys buys me a couple more drinks. Nice chaps.

I lay down for a solid 4 hours of deep sleep. I wake up, shower, and go back downstairs to the bar. Seems that I have walked into a strange occurrence. The girl that served me my drinks earlier is all riled up about her boyfriend that just left. She starts crying. An older guy consoles her. I figure she's just being dramatic, but then the boyfriend storms into the place and starts yelling, cursing, and even draws back his fist at one point like he's gonna punch the guy in front of him. Then he turns to her ready to throw.

Eventually, he gets dragged out by the bouncer and walks away down some corner street. Jerk. In America, the cops would have been called for sure, and he certainly would have gotten his ass kicked by some of

243

the bar gents. An interesting first impression of this country.

After a long trip a few time zones backward into a new land, my mind clock is quite bollixed up in happenstance. I sleep a few dreams for good luck and give the devil what for. Time is still a bit sideways when I wake at the Bloomsbury hour.

Well well well, London town indeed. I go to London Bridge with my new friend Paddington Farnsworth. We have a smashing good time. What a bloke though. I'd bet 3 prawns to the queen's knickers he couldn't box his way out of a Wellington strawberry. The gentry at the fort quarters could use a cricket or two, but the pub wench is quite fine indeed. Not to be a shrug bugger but she gets me randy in the pants something fierce.

Just kidding. I'm only practicing my local dialect. I'm piecing the mystery the election together. It's bigger than I thought. The question we need to ask is where did the porn revolution and the gender transition go to and come from? This is the changing of the queen bee; a sea change of the species bigger than this century and our silly politics. The USA will belong to a woman on Tuesday. To the casual observer the hive activity will remain the same, but inside, the bees will be singing and dancing to a totally different beat. Where there was a line of wasps, there is now a queen. Another queen to join the others. A standard mother by all other accounts. It has been a long time coming. The resistance doesn't make sense to half the drones right now. I don't know how that's gonna play out. I think everything will be fine because everyone should still have porn. I think Donald Trump would take away our porn, but he's going to be thrown off the cliff of Mount Rushmore in four moons.

Could you imagine if our porn got taken away? Eventually, nobody would shave their pubes anymore and would get back to dry humping each other all day. You might not believe me, but it's true. I've done the math with my sex pencil.

Dukes, Queens, Peasants, Nobleman... I should be an expert on the matter when I get back from Britannia. I could see myself settling in

244

London in a few years; maybe Oxford or Cambridge. I'm sure they each have a mailroom I could work at in exchange for free classes. If the queen has a cataclysmic stroke, well so be it. Has to happen sooner or later. Just another celebration as far as I'm concerned. A party of tears. Once I live there I could just surround myself with books, video games, and the buck-toothed royal Susans.

The weather is a little dreary, but other than that this place is beautiful. People speak in a very sing-songy voice. It's endearing. Smart dressers too. I certainly stick out wearing my mountain town clothes. Hard to explain the buzz around this beehive. It's busy, but quiet somehow. Things seem cleaner than they should be. Everything is very organized, even the chaos.

The tubes! Let me tell you about the tubes. That's what they call the subway system here. I'm convinced it was built with advanced alien technology. You go underground down these long escalators. It's a little disorienting because the walls and ceiling come together in a circle. You're in a tube, so if you go down you feel like you're just going forward, the map looks like a circuit board. Several lines to and from each junction. So, you figure out where you are and where you're going and connect the dots. That's pretty standard. The difference is, there are no timetables. The train comes and goes every 2 minutes all day. These things are buzzing all beneath London all day. And when I say buzzing, I mean at light-speed, and at an almost complete silence. The trains are round just like the tunnel. There is maybe an 8-inch gap between the outside of the train in the wall of the tube. It's totally automated. Nobody drives these things. I'm telling you, it's from the future.

The Spoils of 5000 years of plundering and world domination here sitting on shelves all around town. Museums and galleries around every corner and they're all free for admittance. Buildings as big as football stadiums filled with treasure and ancient artifacts. How nice it is sorting through it all during these turbulent times.

I wish my dear friend Melissa was over here walking through these museums with me. She's one of those folks like me that can spend 3 hours in one small room of a huge museum. I learn the basics of reading hieroglyphics in the Egypt exhibit. Turns out that the bird symbols you see everywhere just represent a phonetic sound, a letter. Just like the little box, and the snake looking thing. But these phonetic symbols are sometimes followed by qualifying pictures. We don't have anything like that in our vocabulary. Maybe the closest thing is that trademark or copyright symbols that you see sometimes.

I'm trying to finish writing this stupid book as I bum around town. I have a vision of walking through the quad of one of these fine Ivy League universities as either a student or professor. These types of visions I have pretty much always come to pass or way or another. Vail, prison, Philly, Denver, Rome - I saw them all well in advance. Self-fulfilling prophesies most likely. We'll see how this whole thing turns out as I revise the last chapter. That's why they call it a revision; you see things in a vision, then you see them again in another vision.

Kerfuffle

Like everyone else, I figure Hilary has this election in the bag. I wake up at around 2 am and look at YouTube just to see a little reaction, and breathe a sigh of relief that this thing is over, and we can all get on with it. But the votes are still coming in and it's closer than everyone thought. The newscasters are talking about all of these dramatic far-fetched scenarios. News. Always trying to make you think there are burglars in your neighborhood, and a ten-foot blizzard headed your way. Florida goes red. Around the world, hearts of humanity drop off a cliff and skip to a panicked beat. It's a dead heat now.

A Facebook chat window pops up on my iPad. It's Clair. We watch this madness unfold together in the most romantic way possible. Ohio is lost, Michigan and Wisconsin are up for grabs. Pennsylvania goes from "too close to call" to "up for grabs"; and then it becomes obvious that Pennsylvania is lost too.

November 9th was the 18th day of Brumaire by the French Revolutionary calendar - the day in 1799 when Napoleon Bonaparte led a coup against the revolutionary government, established himself as First Consul and grabbed Europe by the pussy. And on this anniversary Donald J. Trump has won the presidency. Wow.

It's a new dawn for mankind. The hippies all have their ass in a hatch about the whole thing, so that cushions the blow. It'll be a good show anyway. I assume we'll be at war soon enough... probably on our own soil this time. The police state we live in is fierce. If that gets turned against ourselves, then we'll have a scene. Camps. Tribes. Marshal law. New flags. That hilarious red hat that says "make America great again".

I'm sure this scene will be more memorable and terrifying to me than when I watched the twin towers go down on 9/11. To be fair, I was back in the mental hospital at the time fighting through a lithium overdose as the doctor prescribed me a toxic level. Who's crazy now Dr. Alcatraz (as we used to affectionately call her)?!?!?

And now there is a pin. It's true. Dunn wears a pin now. Good ole Dunn.

Lots of hippies are wearing a pin now to symbolize... I don't know, the apocalypse or something like that. So today I'll try to go out and get a pin to wear on my lapel in solidarity with those guys.

Like most of my conversations have started here, the guy next to me at the bar hears me order a beer, picks up my American accent, and chats me up with curiosity about the election. Add to the list of fascinating Brits I am meeting on this trip, one Colonel Mike Russell, MA, MBA, FCILT, MCGI. I don't know what any of those titles mean, but they are written on the business card he hands me. On his long black coat hang medals of valor and honor from decades of service around the globe. I don't get the impression that he's trying to show off the hardware so much. No, I gather that there's some sort of remembrance he's going to or coming from, and he's wearing the regalia as part of the etiquette. His pin has 8 giant shields of service from Kosovo to Iraq to West Point to some sort of congressional medal of recognition. Not that he's telling me about them so much. You could figure most of them out if you have any understanding military pins at all.

He tells me about a Greyhound bus trip he took in his younger years with a companion. They were in Chicago for St Paddy's day, then went south to Montgomery, Georgia in the summertime. An interesting slice of the country to see back in the 60's I guess.

We talk about the Brexit mentality that got us this new leader. He talks about the USA being a new country that's still figuring itself out. He says the same thing about Australia - another former British colony. The colonel tells me he believes that history will judge Obama as the last great leader of this generation. It baffles us how popular it has become to overlook this reality. There's this pervasive idea that Americans had to choose between two bad candidates. I don't know how that got to be the popular thinking either. One has a long history of public service and is clearly very intelligent about the world. The other is a con man. He's a parody of white privilege, greed, and ignorance. He's an unapologetic narcissist that lives out his delusions of grandeur so boldly that the weak minded and uneducated masses believes the dangerous and blatant lies he preaches to them.

In a way though, maybe Trump was the poison pill we needed to swallow to fight the cancer growing in society. Will people be able to continue to defend his ignorance after they see it in action, and soldiers start dying for the wars he gets us into? The alternative would have been Trump TV. Plans were in the works for him to start his own channel when he lost. He was collaborating with the founder of Fox News on this venture. This presidential victory is a minor setback for him I believe. I'm sure he'll find a way to trump his bluff into a historic kerfuffle and salvage a defeat from this victory. There would have been no way to fight the spread of hate and ignorance if he could have stayed on the sidelines lobbing grenades at leadership. At least he'll have to be accountable for his actions now. Duck and cover, mother fucker.

We discuss the prospect of military allegiance to Trump. The red states make up a majority of the military, and soldiers tend to follow bold aggressive leaders like Trump more than level headed intelligent figures like Obama. He noted that our military had a bit of a reluctance to follow Clinton in the 90's as well. Military leadership - it's a fascinating aspect of all societies. I wonder how the colonel feels about the queen and her royal lineage. Brits have such strong emotional attachment to the royal family. It doesn't make sense to me. I guess maybe it's like rooting for your favorite sports team, a regional or family tradition.

Mike and I agree that our democracy is not a perfect system, but that in reality nothing ever has been. It's an evolution. It seems to me that the national decisions we make these days are pretty much like reading oracles like the old time prophets and sages used to do. A leader has been chosen out of the embers of the blood moon sacrifice.

So what is Trump's modus operandi? I don't know. I couldn't possibly get into the mind of a 70-year-old billionaire with kids from ages 7 to 37 that has built his life around stacking up casinos, running beauty pageants, and producing reality TV. He's probably just trying to hold on till he can pay off the devil's ransom. It looks like a blood draw. Everything about him is a short-term tactical maneuver. He watches his name more than anything else I think. He wins long shots on wild gambles, and he never folds. Ever. It works for him though. His truth is a reality for people that repeat his words.

The word Trump has long been associated with traditional games of chance. But now it will be indelibly imprinted on the history of mankind as a longshot bluff and triumph of a villain. To say the word trump while playing cards will cast a whole new meaning once the castle burns down.

Over the last few weeks, I've walked hundreds of miles all around this town. I've found no dilapidated parts. Even down the back streets off the grid feel inviting and safe. London truly is a beautiful European town. I could see myself settling in a place like this. It might be time to wake up and snap back into the world. I think there would be more options for me in London if I decided to move here. There's more opportunity than in a ski town for a person with advanced degrees and a critical mind. I could get creative. And I could be anonymous at any time if I wanted. Around every street corner are 5000 people that I've never seen before. If I want to meet them, I meet them. If we mess around and things don't work out I probably never have to see them or their friends again. There just aren't many ladies to choose from there. There's like 200 single girls in the whole town, and half of them have already slept with a few of the sleaze balls I hang around with. That kind of makes it hard to move forward. Not impossible, but difficult. Not that London wouldn't have its pitfalls too in that regard. How do you differentiate a complete whore from a good catch? I guess they would ask the same of me, and there would be no way for them to be comfortable with the answer. I know it. My history is checkered as a chess board. It's all a bunch of beans. Maybe I'll go pray it away when I get around to it.

Vail's gotten to be a drag in other ways too. I have trouble relating to people that live outside the real world. It was nice for a while, but everyone there is a dreamer, an idealist, optimist, yoga hippie. They just haven't seen the other side yet. A lot of them want to grow up from that life. They want to finish their degrees and get a job doing something other than waiting tables. That's all fine. In the process of chasing those things most of them will end up with a baby and a mortgage, and sail off into the street light sunset. Some might chase that aspiration and find that they can't shake some of the trappings that come with ski town life. Booze, cocaine, chronic injury. For me, though it's been different. I slid in there backward. I dropped out of life and landed there. There are parts of that place that make me envision living there for a long time. But I also feel the misery. And it's out of place in a town like that. I sleep through the days too much there. I'm not appreciating the beauty anymore, and that makes me feel guilty. I'm going through the motions even when I'm gliding down the slopes. The niche job I found myself that seems like the perfect fit for my lifestyle is getting dull. Even the mountain town jobs are becoming corporate and politically correct now. Lame

The weather in London town is usually pretty dreary. That could be a downer, but it could also make me appreciate sunny days more than I do now. I very much prefer dreary to hot anyway. I haven't noticed any bugs or rodents around. Everything is very clean and civil. Easy transportation around the city is abundant, which would be clutch for me moving here without a car. And, this is Europe. I could walk down to the train, plane, or boat depot and hop a short ride to another country if I feel like it. Or maybe I'm just dreaming. Everyone in my imagination knows I don't exist.

I'm going to give it one more go in Vail this winter. I'll watch the USA start to fall off a cliff, then I'll move over to London and get back to being an adult. Basically, I'll swim out to the Titanic to gather a couple belongings, then get back to shore before nightfall tears the vessel in two.

I've become fascinated with the church reformation in the 1500's that basically revolved around King Henry VIII trying to find any method he could to convince himself and the world to believe that his marriage to his original wife wasn't valid. It makes me think of how Sister Mila firmly believes that there is no such thing as an annulment. To her, it is a silly idea with no basis in canon rite. I think to most people it's a silly idea. You can't say that something never happened. You can say that it shouldn't have happened, or you wish it hadn't happened, but that's very different than saying that it never actually happened. That's clearly just self-deception. And honestly it's hurtful to those that are cast away because of it, but see the truth for what it is. I'm a son brought up as a bastard from a marriage that some document says never happened.

The historic lessons of the Church of England monarchy and the Roman Catholic Church keep coming back to people convincing themselves of things that have no basis in reality but instead are supported by untruths intentionally derived for sinister purposes. It's just the way the world turns. Always has been, always will be. And here I am, just a certified lunatic drawing parallels to Fox News and the Salem witch trials. I look back at these historical events and see how the deception was eventually lifted and reality turned bastards to kings, infidels to saints, nobles to beggars, ashes to ashes and dust to dust.

Fin

My last night in London town, and I finally catch up with Flo Stow from Nicaragua. We meet at a bar near her college. We swap some memories about last spring and catch each other up on how our trips played out after we parted. Turns out she linked up with some other tween and they hitchhiked around Honduras and Belize for another month. Now she's a freshman in college having a little trouble relating with classmates that have barely ever ridden the tube without adult supervision. She seems very grown up. A casual observer would believe we are on a date probably. I still dress and act like I'm in my 20's, while she seems less like a psychology student and more like a professor with her makeup and formal clothes. It's natural to relate to each other as equals considering our mutual level of conversation about the world and personal affairs.

After dinner and a few drinks, we decide to venture out for more good times. It's Sunday night but considering it's a big city we figure there are some nightlife shenanigans to be found. She recommends an area on the south end of town, so I say what the heck. I figure she knows where the action is. But it becomes clear that I know London way better than she does at this point. I thought she grew up here, but it turns out she grew up about 50 miles out of the city, and only visited once or twice with her parents.

It's pouring rain when we get off the tube, and nothing is open. I decide it's getting late, and I want to start making my way back to the hostel so that I can get up early for my flight in the morning. I thought she'd go on her way, but she decides to come along. She seems to be up for whatever, but she's a freshman in college for Christ sake. I try not to over think it, and don't want to be rude, so we get a bottle of wine and she comes back to the hostel. I've had the dorm room to myself for the last few nights, so since it's late and everything, we agree that if it's still open she'll stay over. As chance has it there's someone in the bunk next to mine. I'm almost relieved. It was there for the taking, but I think having sex with someone half my age would have been... remarkably regrettable.

253

The return voyages from these backpacking trips are always the worst part. This particular one is off to a terrible start. I'm supposed to fly from London to Denver via Las Vegas; leave in the morning, arrive in the evening. Easy. I made sure I had plenty of time to make my flight when I left my hostel this morning. But I'm an idiot. I went to the wrong airport.

I immediately recognize that the ramifications of missing this flight will be severe, but my flight doesn't leave for two hours so I might still be able to make it. I quickly talk to a couple agents around the airport and find out that the trip from Gatwick airport to Heathrow is about an hour if there's no traffic. You're supposed to be there two hours before takeoff for international flights, but I'm thinking there's still a chance maybe.

It's recommended that I take the bus that leaves in five minutes, so I buy a ticket. The bus doesn't even show up for fifteen minutes, and twenty minutes after that we still haven't left and the driver tells us we're making a couple stops along the way. My chances of making this flight on time are dwindling with every second that ticks away, and I'm sitting here helpless.

A couple other people are in my situation, not because they're idiots like me. They had actual logistical obstacles that they couldn't control. I guess in the end it's all the same. I couldn't control how dumb I was any more than they could control their traffic and flight delays. Anyway, we start asking questions and it turns out we have about a zero chance of getting to Heathrow on time now. Had we been given better information it would be a totally different story. But after a precious half hour of lost time, we decide that there's still a chance of getting there on time if we get a cab. It's obviously expensive to take an hour long cab ride, but it's better than burning a $500 plane ticket and having to book another one that would be way more expensive on short notice and wouldn't leave till who knows when.

It's actually a pleasant ride to Heathrow with my two new friends.

Claudia is a doctor from Norway that works as a doctor on cruise ships. She's a stunning blond haired woman about my age probably. Pierre buys and sells luxury automobiles around Europe. They're both clearly wealthy and attractive, and I wouldn't be surprised if they get a hotel room to fuck in if they miss their flight. Of course, Pierre starts talking about the election. Claudia and I want nothing to do with this conversation, but I strike it up with him. He thinks Donald Trump will be a good leader because of the strength against enemies that he has portrayed. I make the point that there is more strength in avoiding war than pursuing it. It's easy to talk hard and send people off to propagate an endless war, but it takes courage to stand up to the angry mob and preach restraint. He admits that I have changed his perspective. I'm shocked because in all my days I have not once seen a person's opinion swayed by rational ideas.

We arrive at the Heathrow and I run from the cab to the airline counter only to find out that I've missed my check in by ten minutes. What now? I take a seat by one of the arrival gate windows to think this through. I feel like such an idiot. I almost lose it. I'm muttering to myself and bang I can't restrain myself from banging my fist on the chair a couple times. I even punch myself in the head a couple times too. That's a new one, never did that before. Yeah, sometimes if you have these kinds of outbursts in a public place, particularly in an airport, you find yourself locked up in a padded room. I guess I can have pretty intense and alarming reactions to things sometimes, but if I can get through for about an hour or so, it passes. The trouble comes if I have to take immediate consequences in the middle of these short-term episodes. That's when the wheels come off, and life really breaks down.

So I'm in an airport with my backpack on, nowhere to be, nowhere to go. Fuck it. The beauty is that I don't give a fuck... about anything. There's really nothing that anyone can hold over my head to give to me or take away. I guess you might say I'm smart, capable, resourceful, but who really has any need for a person like that in their life? I'm a free radical as they say in the cancer society. I'm thinking maybe I'll go to Greece, maybe China. Who cares, whatever's cheap. Maybe I'd have done it a year or two ago, but at this point, I just want to be back home. I'm getting too old for this shit and I'm tired of the backpacker lifestyle. I find a somewhat reasonable flight to New York that leaves in 5 hours so I book it and figure I'll piece the rest of the way back from there.

It's almost Thanksgiving, and when I land I'll be a couple hour drive from most of my family. What an opportunity to swoop in unexpectedly and surprise the bunch, patch things up with everyone, reunite. Reality sets in. The prospect of trying to make my way from the airport via buses and trains to any scrap of a family that might have me for dinner is difficult, depressing, and basically pointless. I remember, I'm banished and forgotten, and my last three attempts to get an invite from mom to the family gathering at her house have been aggressively denied. Son of a bitch. It's ok. I'm just going to pretend I'm back in the nut house. I often sort of fantasize about being back in there anyway. Helpless and alone for days or weeks with no end in sight, no way out, and nothing I can do to improve my situation. Just surrender.

I replay today's events in my head and accept my careless mistake as basically just a minor inconvenience in the grand scheme of things. I come to recognize that I've made so many mistakes along the way that have led me here. But it's not a good place. I suppose looking back that my attempt to shake up the family in order to shine a light on the past has irrevocably backfired. I'm banished now and I just need to accept it. As for the brothers, I'm just not one of them. I never was. All this time I was trying to get ma to acknowledge that and change it, but we both know there is no changing the situation. It has probably been pretty sad watching me struggle to accept this. Well, I get it now. I have no one. No family, no close friends, and these trips are not liberating me or making my life better or richer in any way. So this will be the last time I go wandering around by myself. I'm done with all this nonsense. It'll be much easier to travel in my imagination from now on. I know what sand feels like. I don't need to travel hundreds of miles to sit on it. Exotic food is easy to make, especially the kind I end up buying on these trips - street vendor food. Museums. Waste of time. I can look all this stuff up on the Internet. And after you see a few natural wonders you really don't need to go to the rest. Maybe the pictures don't do them justice, but if you know that from experience, then you can get the idea when you look at pictures of places you haven't been to yet.

So that's that. I think I'll quit my job when I get back if I'm not already fired. I'm giving up this way of life. I'm ready to grow up and be an adult again. I'm going to try to find a job that doesn't require me to speak to anyone. I'm going to get back to doing paperwork for a living. I'll take the first job I find in anywhere, USA. I'll sign up for a 30-year mortgage on a shitty one bedroom condo 12 miles from my suburban office and focus on being average. I'll play the lottery twice each week so that I can add some extra excitement to my nightly routine of watching Seinfeld re-runs and the evening sports highlights. Hopefully, I never win though or else I'll be right back here where I started, doing leisure activities all day, traveling the world like an idiot, and writing a memoir of my pointless thoughts as if anyone gives half a damn.

fin

Proof

Made in the USA
Columbia, SC
16 July 2017